Introduction

The departure of the Roman legions in AD410 left Britain vulnerable to a wide variety of raiders: the Picts from Scotland, the Scots from Ireland, and the Angles, Saxons and Jutes from northern Europe. However, a British leader called Vortigern managed to organise the native forces well enough to keep the raiders at bay. Unfortunately, in AD445, a plague epidemic seriously weakened his control. In the following year, the Picts' raids recommenced in northern Britain and the Irish invaded West Wales. In desperation, Vortigern invited Anglo-Saxon mercenaries, led by Hengest and Horsa, to help him fight the raiders. They liked the country so much that they revolted against Vortigern and invaded the country in large numbers.

However, there was an interruption of the Anglo-Saxon invasion of Britain at this point. The details of what happened will probably never be known, as the events of this period are shrouded in the mists of what we call 'The Dark Ages'. They are called 'dark' because there is very little evidence to throw light on what actually occurred. It seems that there was a successful British resistance led by Aurelius Ambrosius and the even more legendary figure of King Arthur.

From about AD500 the Anglo-Saxon conquest was complete. The Anglo-Saxons went on to build one of the finest cultures of continental Europe, with outstanding achievements in scholarship, literature, art and architecture.

In AD793, a Viking raid on the monastery of Lindisfarne marked the beginning of a new wave of invasions, this time by the Danes and Norwegians. King Alfred the Great managed to prevent them conquering the whole country, by a series of victories which confined them to the north-east of the country, called 'The Danelaw'. However, during the reign of King Knut (AD1017-35), all England fell under Danish rule. This was not as big a disaster as the Norman conquest of AD1066 because the Anglo-Saxons and the Danes shared a similar culture. Indeed, the Danish influence made a positive contribution to art, literature and language.

The Norman conquest of AD1066 ended forever many aspects of Anglo-Saxon life. Most of the nobility, both secular and religious, were replaced by their Norman counterparts. Even the English language was lost for a time (the official languages of the country being French and Latin). The Norman ruling class was a minority of the population, and they gradually adapted to Anglo-Saxon culture, eventually losing their own language. Thus the study of the Anglo-Saxons is not the study of a dead culture, but of a culture that still has a profound influence on the Britain of today.

The activity sheets in this book cover key aspects of the political, religious, social and cultural life of the Anglo-Saxons, in a way that brings history to life through practical activity, discussion and writing. Wherever possible, source materials are presented as a basis for these activities.

Invade Britain - Ideas Page

Aim

To help the children understand some of the reasons for the Anglo-Saxon invasions.

Preparation

- Introduce the children to the reasons for the invasions.
- Compare the map on the activity sheet with a modern map of Europe.
  - Which parts do the children recognise from the activity sheet map?
  - What major changes have there been?

Developments

- Show the children a map of modern Europe.
  - What is Angeln called today? (Denmark)
  - What is Frisia called today? (Holland)
- Ask the children to use a map of the British Isles to find place names with the endings shown below. Explain that they are Anglo- Saxon and have their own meanings.

Counties	Place names
sex – comes from the word Saxon	**ford** – river crossing **wich** – farm **ham** – village **ings** – followers of (eg **Hast**ings is named after the followers of Haesta)

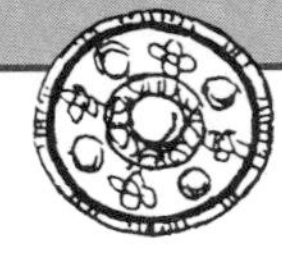

Background

Reasons for the invasions:
- Before AD410, the Roman Army had protected Britain from invasion by sea, by using their fleet and building fortresses along the southern and eastern coasts. However, in this year, the Roman Emperor Honorius told the British that they must defend themselves, as the Roman army was needed to fight the Gauls. This meant that Britain was left open to attack.
- Britain was a wealthy country. It had slaves, gold and jewellery, and its land was fertile.
- Parts of Germany and Scandinavia were over populated.

Activities

- To play the 'Invade Britain' game (for groups of four):
  - Photocopy one game board per group (if possible to A3).
  - The children cut out and colour the counters.
  - Counters are placed face down and chosen at random.
  - Each child then places a counter on the START square of the appropriate route.
  - The children ask each other questions about the Anglo-Saxons. If they are right they roll the dice and can move forward that number of squares.
- Consolidate the children's knowledge of the invasions by asking them:
  - Why did the Anglo-Saxons invade Britain?
  - Which tribes attacked Britain and where did they raid?
  - Why were the Anglo-Saxons successful?
- The groups of four could invent a story of their invasion adventures and share this with the rest of the class.
- Use the board game to give structure to their story writing.

- The first Anglo-Saxon settlers sent messages to their friends persuading them to come to Britain. The children could work in small groups to make a chart to explain the attractions of coming to Britain. These prompt s may be useful.
  - good farmland
  - good grass for cattle to graze on
  - clear rivers
  - good vineyards
  - poor defences.

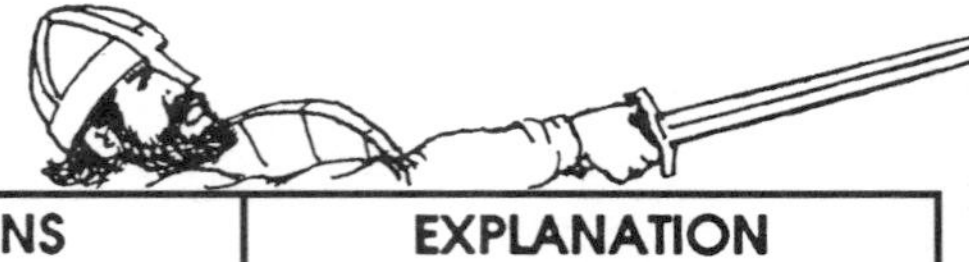

ATTRACTIONS	EXPLANATION

14.95

FOLENS IDEAS BANK ANGLO-SAXONS

Chris Webster

Contents

How to use this book

Ideas Bank books provide ready to use, practical, photocopiable activity pages for children, **plus** a wealth of ideas for extension and development.

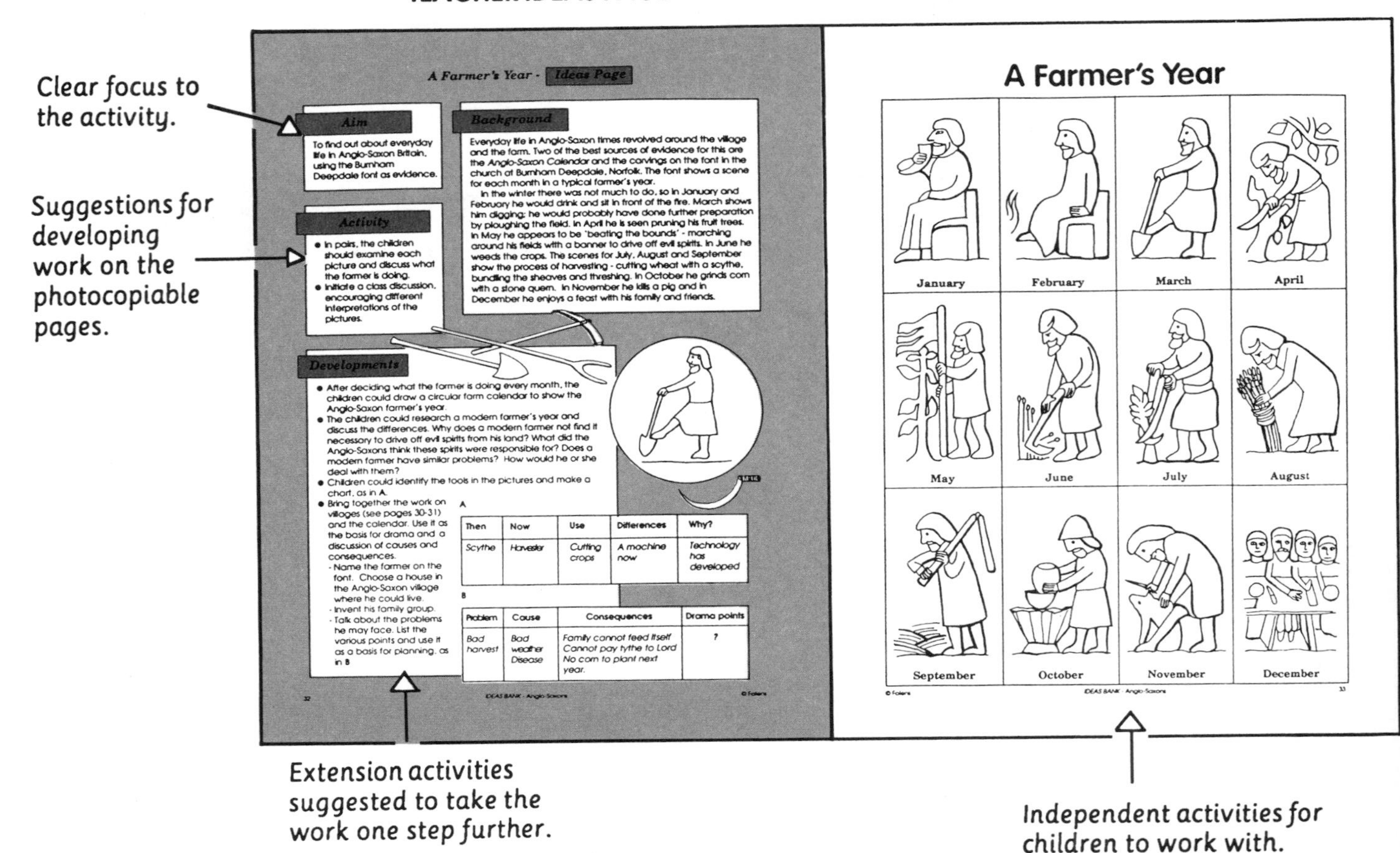

- Time-saving, relevant and practical, **Ideas Bank** books ensure that you will always have work readily to hand.

Editor: Angela Simms. Illustrations by: Tony Dover and Peter Broadbent. Cover by: In Touch Creative Designs Limited. Cover Photo: Michael Holroyd. Printed by Craft Print Pte Ltd.

First published 1994 by Folens Limited, Albert House, Apex Business Centre, Boscombe Road, Dunstable, LU5 4RL, England.

ISBN 185276542-9

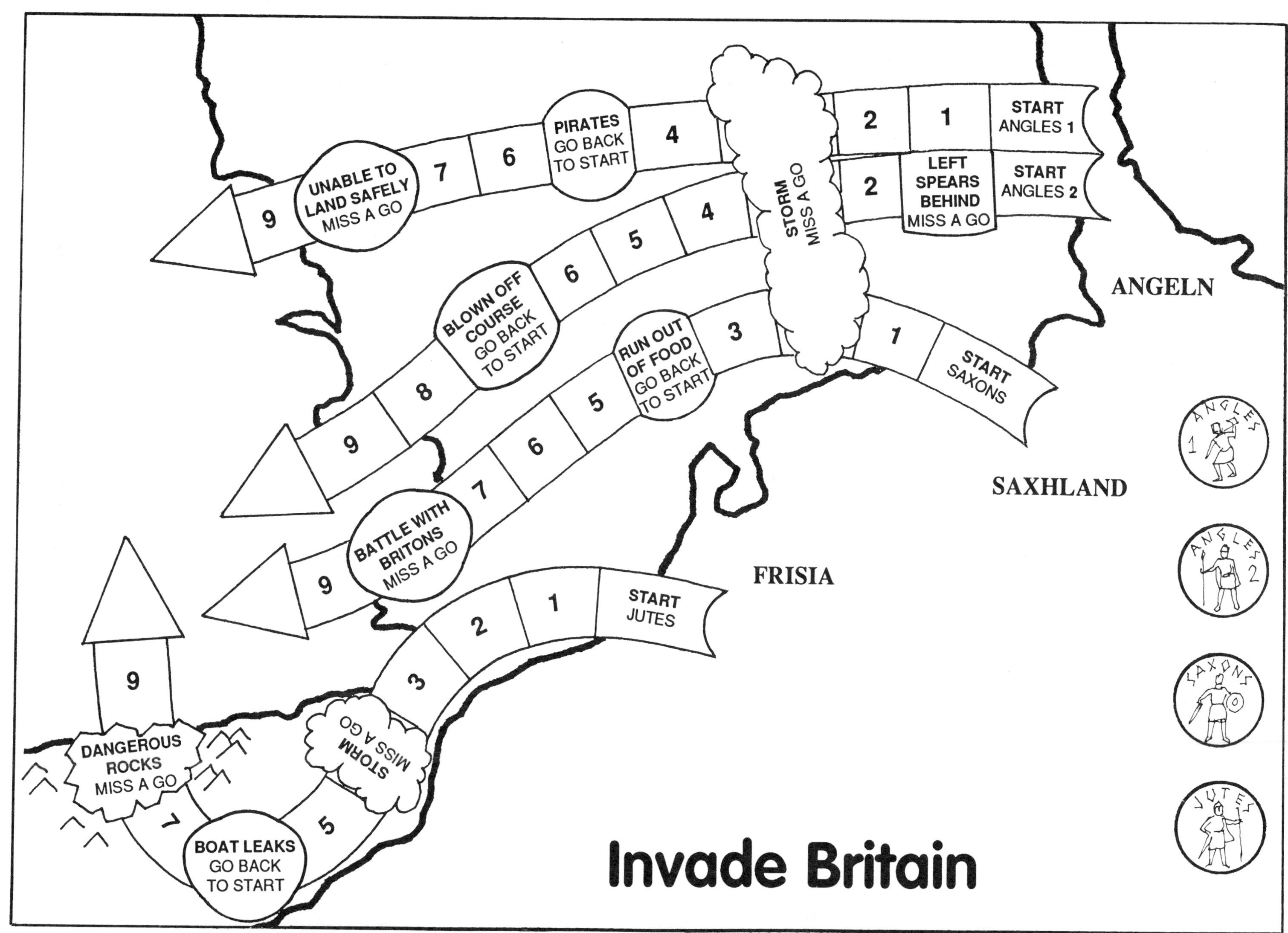
Invade Britain
START
ANGLES 1
1
2
4
PIRATES
GO BACK
TO START
6
7
UNABLE TO
LAND SAFELY
MISS A GO
9
START
ANGLES 2
LEFT
SPEARS
BEHIND
MISS A GO
2
STORM
MISS A GO
4
5
6
BLOWN OFF
COURSE
GO BACK
TO START
8
9
START
SAXONS
1
3
RUN OUT
OF FOOD
GO BACK
TO START
5
6
7
BATTLE WITH
BRITONS
MISS A GO
9
START
JUTES
1
2
3
STORM
MISS A GO
5
BOAT LEAKS
GO BACK
TO START
7
DANGEROUS
ROCKS
MISS A GO
9
ANGELN
SAXHLAND
FRISIA
ANGLES 1
ANGLES 2
SAXONS
JUTES

Hengest Adventure Game - Ideas Page

Aim

To introduce the children to one of the most important events in English history: the landing of Hengest and Horsa in AD449.

Preparation

- The children will need to be provided with some information about:
  - the geography of Saxon settlements (see pages 14-15)
  - arms and armour (see page 26)
  - the Picts.

Activity

- To play the game:
  - Divide the class into pairs.
  - The children cut out the game cards, write the number of each card on the back and lay them out face-down in order.
  - They take it in turns to read out the cards.
  - Card 1 is read out, discussed and a decision made. They will then take the appropriate card according to the decision they have made.
  - The game is won when they reach Card 7. They should then read Card 8 to complete the story.

Background

AD449 marks the first large scale settlement of Anglo-Saxons in Britain. King Vortigern of Britain needed more warriors to help him fight the Picts who were threatening Britain from the north. He hired Anglo-Saxon mercenaries (Hengest, Horsa and their followers) who were to be rewarded in gold or land.

In Roman times, the Picts had been held back by Hadrian's Wall, which stretched from the Tyne to Solway, and had formed the effective northern boundary of Roman civil and military rule in Britain. However, with the absence of the Roman army this physical boundary was no longer sufficient to stop the Picts.

This game is based on the information given in the *Anglo-Saxon Chronicle*, though card 8 draws on later sources such as *Historia Brittonum* (written around the ninth century), which is attributed to one of its editors, Nennius.

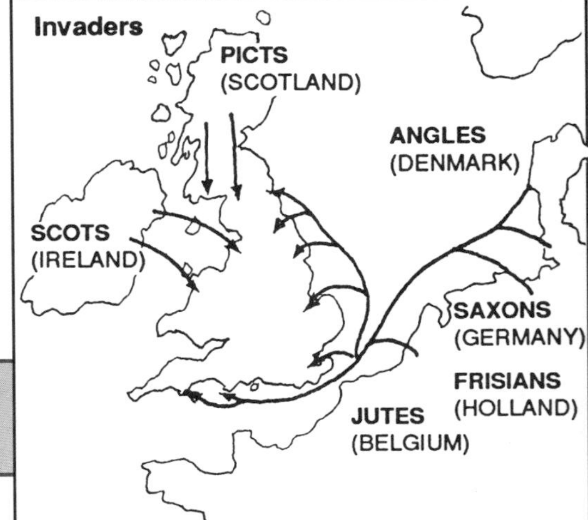

Developments

- The game may have a variety of outcomes. To find out what actually happened, ask the children to lay out cards 1, 3, 4 and 5 and read them again. They could use the actual historical sequence as a basis for other activities.
- Make an illustrated version of the game. Cut out 8 pieces of card which are twice the size of the game squares. The children paste the writing on one half of each card and illustrate the information on the other half.
- Ask the children to imagine they are monks and write a short 'Chronicle' for the year AD449 (cards 1, 3, 4 and 5). They could decorate the pages as the monks did (see page 46). If possible, provide them with dip-in pens or quills.
- Use the game as the basis for a story. Provide the children with suggestions for the beginning:

With a great cheer the ropes were cast off, and the ships rowed out to sea. Hengest and his men were so excited by their adventure that they didn't notice the storm clouds...

Hengest - Adventure Game

1. START

It is the year 449. You are a warrior called Hengest in a country called Angeln. You have a brother called Horsa and a large band of followers who are eager for adventure.

What will you do?

SAIL TO BRITAIN (4) **OR** *STAY AT HOME (2)*

2. STAY AT HOME

Your followers are eager for adventure. They call you a coward and elect your brother Horsa as leader. Horsa takes them to Britain.

END OF GAME

Try again and be more courageous!

3. TALK

The British leader asks you who you are and what you want. You tell him that you are seeking adventure.

He says that his king, King Vortigern, will give you and your men a great reward if you will fight for him.

What will you do?

ACCEPT (5) **OR** *REFUSE (6)*

4. SAIL TO BRITAIN

After a cold, stormy voyage you land at a place called Ebsfleet. The shore is lined with Britons. They have twice as many warriors, many of them on horses.

What will you do?

FIGHT (7) **OR** *TALK (3)*

5. ACCEPT

You join forces with the British. You march north and fight the Picts.

You win easily and King Vortigern gives you great rewards.

YOU HAVE WON THE GAME!

To find out what happened to Hengest, read card 8.

6. REFUSE

The British leader says that he must drive you back into the sea because you have refused his offer.

You are defeated and killed.

END OF GAME

I thought you were seeking adventure! Try again.

7. FIGHT

Your men are cold and weary. They do not have horses and they are outnumbered two to one. You are defeated and killed.

END OF GAME

You showed great courage, but use your common sense next time! Try again.

8. END

Hengest's daughter, Rowena, married King Vortigern. This made the British nobles angry because they were Christians but Hengest and Rowena were pagans. The British nobles led a rebellion. There were many battles and eventually Hengest was defeated and beheaded.

However, many Anglo-Saxons survived, and many more came to settle. Over the next two hundred years they conquered most of Britain and gave it a new name, Angle Land - England.

King Arthur - the Evidence - Ideas Page

Aim

To explore the legend of King Arthur in the light of the evidence and to introduce the children to the idea of historical interpretation.

Background

The first large scale Anglo-Saxon settlement began in AD449, led by Hengest and Horsa (see pages 6 and 7). However, it was another seventy years before they made further headway under Cerdic and Cynric (two Saxon chieftains from whom Alfred and his line claimed descent). What held them back for so long? Some people believe that the legend of King Arthur offers an explanation. Underlying the legend of a knight in shining armour living in a fairy-tale castle at Camelot could be the historical reality of a king or general who rallied the Britons against the Anglo-Saxons.

Developments

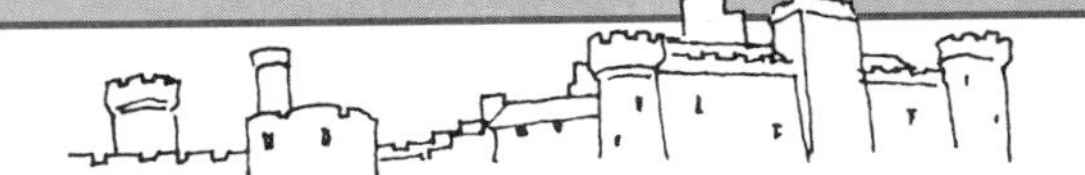

- Ask the children to describe how King Arthur may have appeared and acted.
- Collect pictures of King Arthur from various sources and ask children their opinions on what sort of man Arthur appears to be. For example, Thomas Malory's *Le Morte D'Arthur* portrays a romantic view of King Arthur.
- Discuss whether or not King Arthur existed. What evidence might there be?
- Compare legends with reality.

King Arthur - the legend	King Arthur - the reality
A knight in shining armour. His armour is usually shown as full armour plate.	Full plate armour was not invented until the fourteenth century. He would have worn the armour of the time - a helmet, chain-mail shirt and shield.
He lived in a magnificent castle with many towers and turrets.	He probably lived in a refortified hill fort.

Activity

- The first two pieces of evidence are unreliable, and probably forgeries. The last is not so easily dismissed and enables us to glimpse the 'real' King Arthur.
- The children could discuss the evidence in groups. Then, bring the class together to talk about the conclusions they have reached.

An extract from the Welsh Annals:

447	*Days as dark as night.*
453	*Easter altered on the Lord's Day by Pope Leo, Bishop of Rome.*
454	*St. Brigid is born.*
457	*St. Patrick goes to the Lord.*
458	*St. David is born in the thirtieth year after Patrick left Menevia.*
468	*The death of Bishop Benignus.*
501	*Bishop Ebur rests in Christ. He was 350 years old.*
516	*The Battle of Badon, in which Arthur carried the Cross of our Lord Jesus Christ for three days and three nights on his shoulders and the Britons were the victors.*
521	*St. Columba is born. The death of St. Brigid.*
537	*The battle of Camlann, in which Arthur and Medraut fell and there was plague in Britain and Ireland.*
544	*The sleep of Giaran.*
547	*The great death in which Maelgwn, King of Gwynedd died. Thus they say 'The long sleep of Maelgwn in the court of Rhos'. Then was the yellow plague.*
558	*The death of Gabrán, son of Dungart.*
562	*Columba went to Britain.*

The Welsh Annals

The Welsh Annals are a list of the main events in the early history of Wales. They are from a ninth century source (*Historia Brittonum* by Nennius). A translation is given here.

- Discuss this list of events with the children:
  - What do they tell us about King Arthur?
  - What else do they tell us about life during this period?

King Arthur - the Evidence

1. The Glastonbury Cross
In AD1278 at Glastonbury Abbey, a tomb, thought to be that of King Arthur, was opened. It contained the bones of a man and his wife and this engraved cross.

- Find the words 'Rex Arturius' (which mean 'King Arthur' in Latin).

Unfortunately the cross has been lost. All that is left is a seventeenth-century drawing.

2. The Round Table
At Winchester Castle there is a round table which is said to have been King Arthur's.

- Why is a Tudor rose painted in the middle? Could wood have lasted this long?

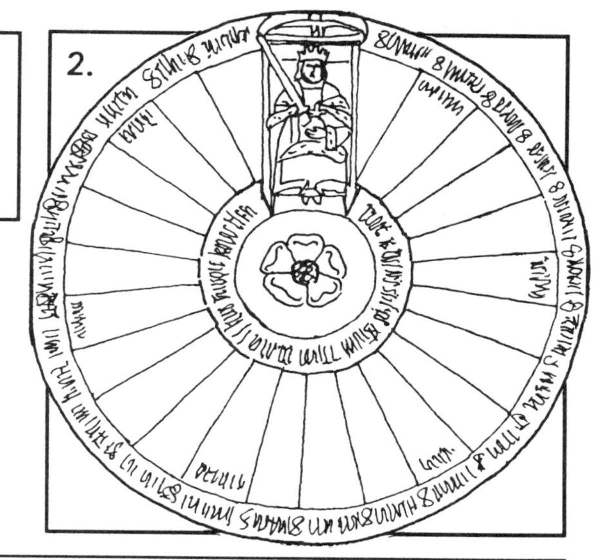

3. Cadbury Castle
This is an artist's impression of a hill fort at Cadbury Castle near Glastonbury. Excavations in 1966 (see A-B and C-D in diagram) proved that the fortifications had been rebuilt during the time when King Arthur lived.

- Could Cadbury Castle be Camelot?

The fortifications may have looked like this.

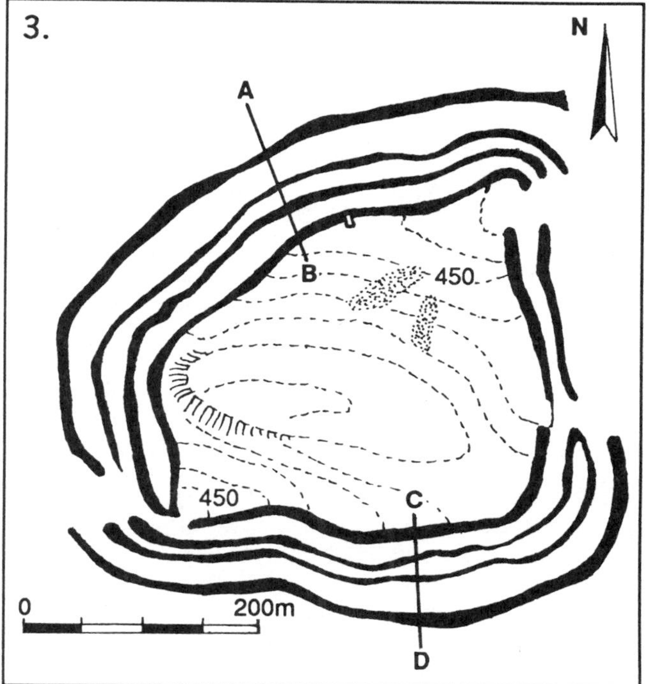

Fight the Danes! - Ideas Page

Aim

To give the children a basic knowledge of King Alfred's long struggle to defeat the Danes.

Background

The Danish invasion falls into two distinct periods. During the first phase, a large army, led by Guthrum, attempted to settle in England (AD870). King Alfred managed to prevent them from conquering the whole country by winning the Battle of Edington (AD878). Alfred signed a treaty with Guthrum to divide England. The north-east part, called the 'Danelaw' being ruled by the Danes. The second phase of the invasion took place between AD892 and AD895 when another Danish army attempted to invade England.

Activity

- This game aims to teach the children about the significant features of the invasion:
  - the large number of battles fought
  - the leadership of King Alfred
  - the establishment of the Danelaw.
- The children should work in pairs.
  - They toss a coin to decide which player is the Dane and which is Alfred.
  - The counters can be cut out, or use coins: tail side up for the Danes, head side up for King Alfred.
  - Each player places several coins outside the playing area.
  - The Danes move first. A counter is placed on any battlefield.
  - King Alfred places a counter over it.
  - A coin is tossed to decide the winner of the battle. The loser is removed from play and the winner left on the battlefield.
  - The game goes on until every battle has been fought.
  - If King Alfred wins seven battles or more, the dotted line marking the Danelaw can be drawn and the Danes must retreat behind it.
  - If the Danes win, the whole of Britain becomes Danelaw.

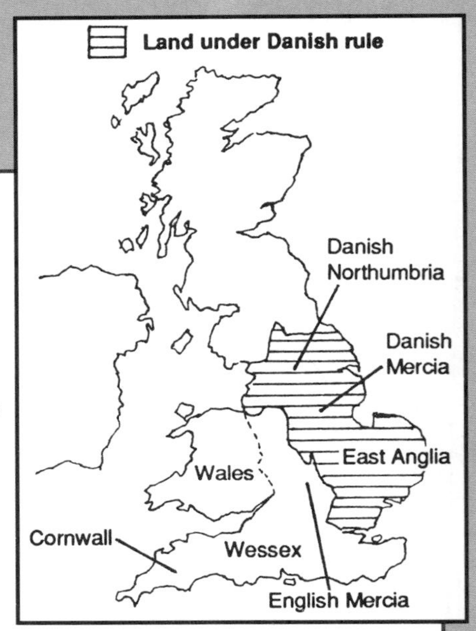

Developments

- Find the battle sites on a modern map of England.
- Ask the children to find out more about one of the battles.
- Anglo-Saxon battle poetry can be a useful historical source. Read extracts **A** and **B**.

A

Storming the building he burst the portal
Though fashioned of iron with fiendish strength;
Forced open the entrance in savage fury
And rushed in rage o'er the shining floor.
A baleful glare from his eyes was gleaming
Most like to a flame.

from ***Beowulf***

B

Byrhtnoth commanded his men to make a wall of shields and the Vikings attacked. Men shouted, swords clashed on shields, spears like a shower, but the English shield wall stood steadfast under the onslaught. Seeing this, Byrhtnoth encouraged his men to win glory and led forward...another spear hit. Wulfmaer pulled the spear from Byrhtnoth's body and flung it back at the Viking. It went straight through him. Then another of the seafarers went for Byrhtnoth, drew his sword and struck at his ring mail shirt, but as he did this, another Viking almost hacked his arm off. Blood gushed from the wound, and his golden hilted sword fell useless to the ground.

from a translation of the ***Battle of Maldon***

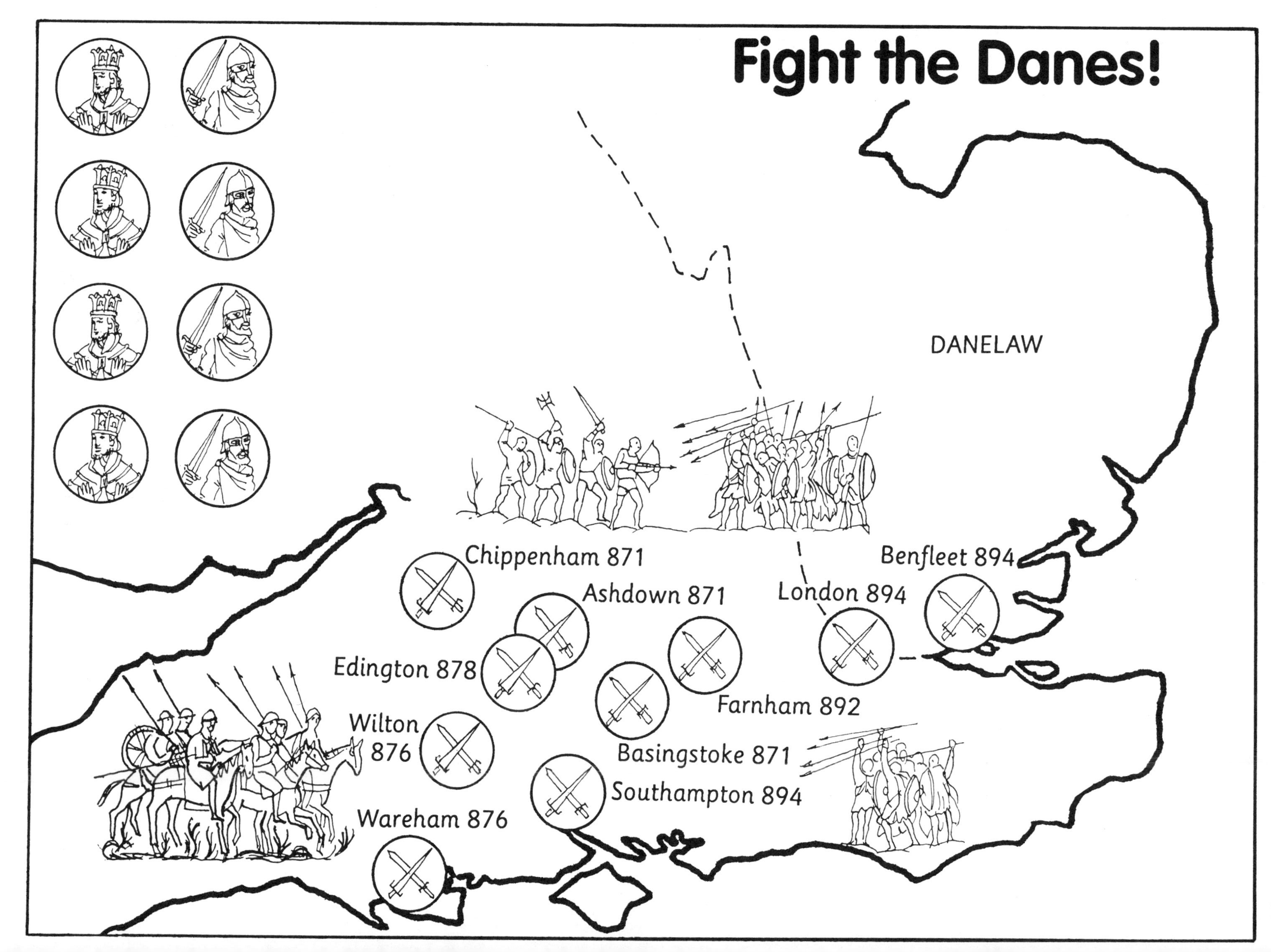
Fight the Danes!
DANELAW
Chippenham 871
Ashdown 871
London 894
Benfleet 894
Edington 878
Farnham 892
Wilton 876
Basingstoke 871
Southampton 894
Wareham 876

King Alfred the Great - Ideas Page

Aim

To introduce the children to the major achievements of Alfred the Great's life.

Activity

- To play the game:
  - Cut out the four cards.
  - The children play in pairs, taking it in turns to read the cards aloud and to discuss their decision.
  - When four decisions have been reached the bottom strip is read.

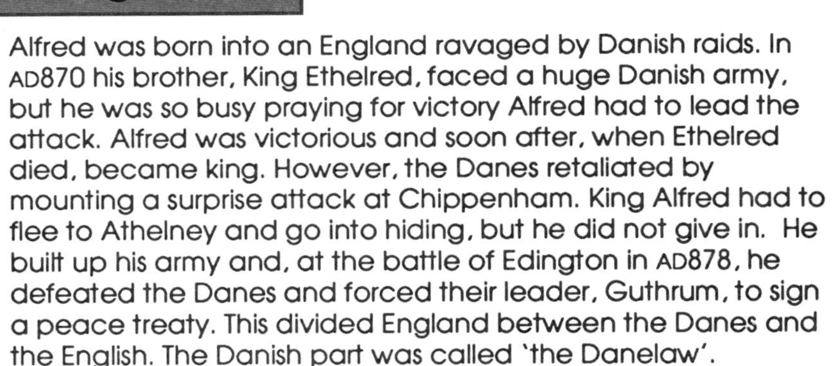

Background

Alfred was born into an England ravaged by Danish raids. In AD870 his brother, King Ethelred, faced a huge Danish army, but he was so busy praying for victory Alfred had to lead the attack. Alfred was victorious and soon after, when Ethelred died, became king. However, the Danes retaliated by mounting a surprise attack at Chippenham. King Alfred had to flee to Athelney and go into hiding, but he did not give in. He built up his army and, at the battle of Edington in AD878, he defeated the Danes and forced their leader, Guthrum, to sign a peace treaty. This divided England between the Danes and the English. The Danish part was called 'the Danelaw'.
King Alfred would have been remembered as a great king for these achievements alone, but he also encouraged the development of law, art and literature. He is the only English king to have been given the title 'The Great'.

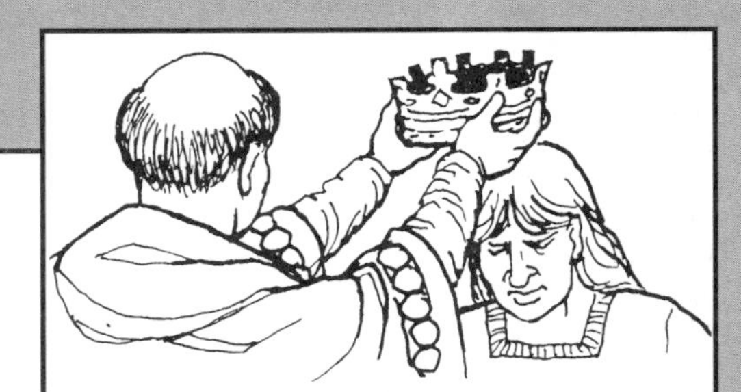

Easter AD871 - Ethelred dies and Alfred becomes king.

Developments

- Suggest that the children research the life of the King. They could draw a picture sequence of the main events in Alfred's life, and write suitable captions for each. These could be displayed and versions compared:
  - Why are some episodes more important to some children?
  - King Alfred is famous for burning the cakes. Is this really an important event in his life?
  - Can this be proved to be fact or is it just a legend?
- Alfred encouraged people to read and write. He set up a school in his palace and ordered bishops to translate the Bible into English. Discuss the following extract:

> *All young people who are now in England free-born, who have the aptitude to apply themselves, should be set to learning ... until they can fully understand how to read English writing.*
>
> ***Alfred***

King Alfred hides in a peasant's cottage in Athelney marsh. The peasant woman tells him to watch her cakes while she goes out.

- The children could discuss the answers to these questions and then complete the table.
  - What other kinds of writing were there? (Latin/runes)
  - Where would people learn to read the Bible? (Schools/ monasteries)
  - Who would learn to write - men and women? (Yes)
  - What does 'free-born' tell us? (That slavery existed.)

Alfred's time	Today
Writing in Latin and runes	
Learning by reading the Bible	

You are King Alfred!

It is 870 in Ashdown, Kent. Before you is a huge Danish army. Suddenly, the Danes attack. Your brother Ethelred is praying for victory and refuses to stop praying and lead the army.

Will you:
- **A)** lead the army yourself?
- **B)** make your brother take notice?
- **C)** wait patiently for him to finish?

You are worried that few people can read and write. Other worries are that the Danes are constantly attacking Wessex, and farms and villages are being destroyed.

Will you:
- **A)** encourage people to learn to read and write, as well as fighting the Danes?
- **B)** concentrate on fighting the Danes?
- **C)** concentrate on encouraging people to read and write?

It is January 877. The Danes never fight in Winter, so you are enjoying a great feast in your hall at Chippenham. Suddenly the doors burst open and the Danes charge in, killing your helpless followers. You flee and find safety at Athelney in the Somerset marshes. Meanwhile Wessex is being overrun.

Do you?
- **A)** fight on somehow?
- **B)** pay the Danes to go away as previous kings have done?
- **C)** surrender?

Easter of the year 878 has just passed and you have won a great battle against the Danes at Edington. However, there are still many Danes left in Britain.

Will you:
- **A)** kill their leader, Guthrum, and try to drive out the rest?
- **B)** spare Guthrum in return for a peace treaty?
- **C)** set Guthrum free?

SCORE

Mainly As: You have great powers of leadership and are not afraid to take risks. You would have done as well as King Alfred. England would be safe in your hands.
Mainly Bs: (or a mixture of A's, B's and C's) Your powers of leadership are average.
Mainly Cs: It is lucky you were not King Alfred or the Danes would have had an easy victory!

Anglo-Saxon Kingdoms - Ideas Page

Aim

To understand how England came to be divided into different regions.

Activity

- The jigsaw on the activity sheet introduces the children to the geography of Anglo-Saxon England.
- Divide the class into pairs.
- Cut out the jigsaw pieces. Use the map as a guide and paste the pieces on to a sheet of paper.
- Emphasise the boundaries and mark in the names of the kingdoms, cities and rivers. Each kingdom could be shaded in a different colour. Use one shade to represent all the remaining Celtic areas.
- Ask the children to mark their home town on the map and to identify which Anglo-Saxon kingdom or Celtic area it was in.

Background

By AD650 most of Britain had been conquered by the Saxons. The Anglo-Saxons divided Britain (except Wales and a few other Celtic areas) into seven kingdoms. Kent was the first to develop, but was overtaken in importance by Northumbria in the seventh century. Mercia became supreme in the eighth century. But the golden age of Anglo-Saxon England was the ninth century when Wessex, under the leadership of King Alfred the Great, resisted the might of the Danes. The divisions of land in this period still survive today in county boundaries.

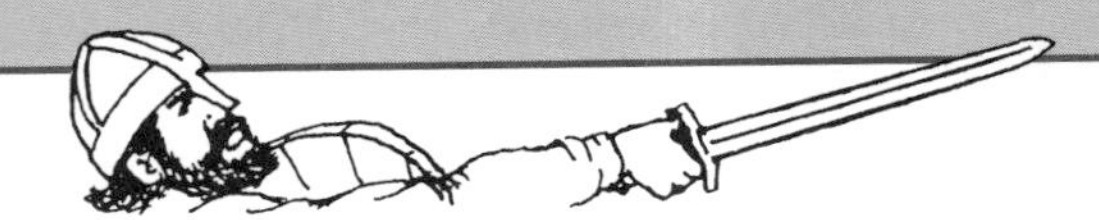

Developments

- Explain that King Offa, the ruler of Mercia, strengthened his kingdom by having a huge ditch and bank built, stretching 148 miles. Look at the map on the activity sheet.
  - Ask the children to list reasons why the King should need to do such a thing.
  - Discuss how easy or difficult it would have been to build Offa's Dyke.
  - Ask them to look in an atlas and trace the boundary of the kingdom. (It goes from Chepstow to Prestatyn along the boundary between Wales and England.)
- Discuss how Anglo-Saxon kingdoms were governed. Introduce diagram **A** and use these questions for discussion.
  - What does it reveal about the people's position in Anglo-Saxon society?
  - How did all these people depend upon each other?
  - How is this system of government different from the one we have today?
- Make a wall display using an enlarged version of the map.
  - Give groups of children pieces of the jigsaw.
  - They could research each kingdom and write their findings a piece of the jigsaw.
  - Assemble the pieces on the wall.

A

King

The Witan
Nobles who advised the king on matters of war, peace and laws.

Thanes
Knights given land by the Witan in return for supplying an army in time of war.

The farmers and peasants
Given land to farm by the Thanes in return for military training (the fyrd).

KINGDOM	RESEARCH SUGGESTIONS
Kent	Hengest
Northumbria	Caedmon
Mercia	Aethelflaed
Wessex	King Alfred
Sussex	The Battle of Hastings
Essex	The Battle of Maldon
East Anglia	Hereward the Wake

The Anglo-Saxon Kingdoms

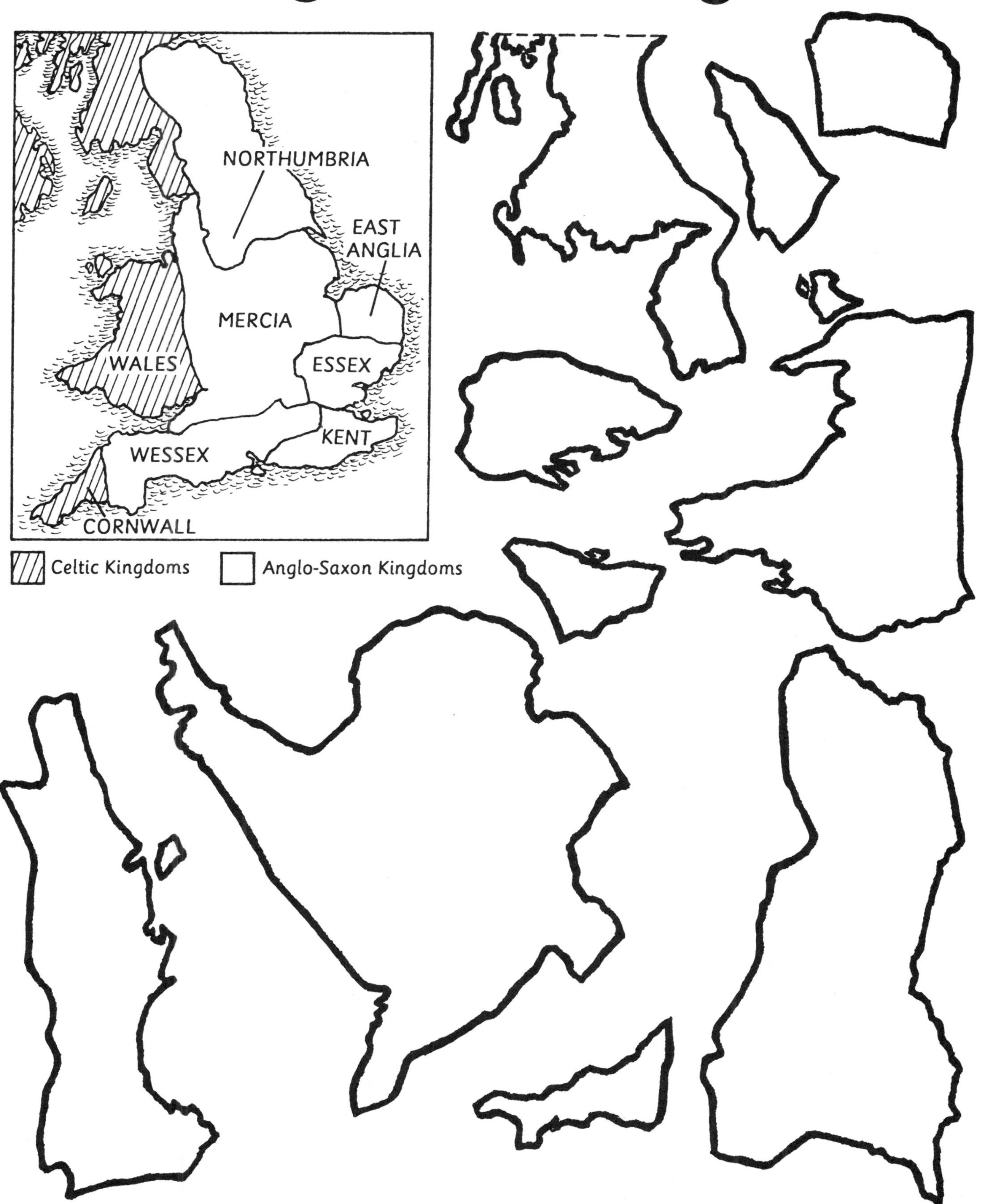

The Norman Conquest - Ideas Page

Aim

To introduce the children to the events of the Norman conquest and to study a famous historical source, the Bayeux Tapestry.

Activity

- Read aloud the story of the Norman invasion.
- The children could work in pairs on an activity sheet which has been cut into strips. They should try to sequence the strips.
- Ask them to identify what is happening in each of the pictures.
- They could then make a mini-tapestry, by glueing the strips end to end and colouring them.

Background

This account of the conquest gives the relevant information (in order) for the sections of the Tapestry shown on the activity sheet.

Duke William heard the news that King Edward the Confessor had died, and he started making preparations to invade England. Ships were built and troops armed, and the fleet set sail for England.

The Normans landed at Hastings, built a fort and attacked surrounding settlements. King Harold of England heard the news while he was fighting the Norwegians at the battle of Stamford bridge. It took twelve days for the English army to march to Hastings.

At Hastings, the English army fell into a defensive shield wall formation against the Normans' attack on horseback. At one point, the Normans fearing defeat, turned and fled. Unwisely, some of the English broke ranks and charged after them breaking the defensive shield wall.

The turning point of the battle was when Harold was fatally wounded when he was allegedly struck in the eye by an arrow. Finding themselves leaderless, many of the English fled. Duke William had won a decisive victory. He was crowned king at Westminster Abbey on Christmas Day AD 1066, a date which is seen as marking the end of the Anglo-Saxon period.

The Bayeux Tapestry was made to the order of Bishop Odo of Bayeux, Duke William's half-brother. Despite its name the Tapestry is really a piece of embroidery, thought to have been sewn by Anglo-Saxon craftswomen in Kent.

Developments

- Ask the children to write out the events of the Norman conquest in chronological order, using the activity sheet.
- This information could be then be represented in the form of a cause and consequence chart, such as the one shown here.
- The Bayeux Tapestry is one of the main sources of evidence for this period. Ask the children to study their tapestry and write notes on the following:
  - everyday clothes
  - ship design
  - tools
  - buildings
  - arms and armour.
- This information could form the basis of a story of the battle from either the Normans' or the Saxons' point of view, bringing out the differences between the two sides.

CAUSE	CONSEQUENCE
Duke William learns Edward the Confessor is dead.	*He makes preparation to invade Britain.*

- Ask members of the class to research:
  - how the British defended their towns
  - what types of weapons were used
  - which character is King Harold. What evidence can the children find that suggests this?

The Norman Conquest

- Cut out the strips and put them in the correct order.

Anglo-Saxon Religion - Ideas Page

Aim

To give the children a basic knowledge of the more well-known Anglo-Saxon gods and goddesses.

Activity

- The activity sheet gives information about some of the most important Anglo-Saxon gods and goddesses (Saturn shows Roman influence).
- The children should match each picture to the correct information and complete the table.

Background

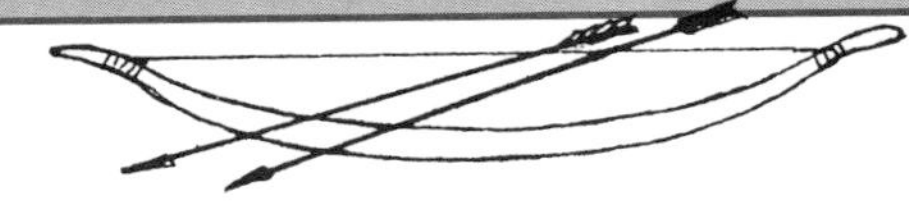

The Anglo-Saxons' religious beliefs originated in their Nordic homelands and were shared by most Germanic cultures. There were slight differences, such as the names of the dieties. The chief god was called Odin by the Norsemen, Wotan by the Germans and Woden by the Anglo-Saxons.

The gods were said to live on a mountain called Asgard in a hall called Valhalla. There were many different gods, each one looking after an aspect of human life. There was no life after death, except for the warrior who died in battle. He would be taken from the battlefield to Valhalla by a Valkyrie. There he would live a life of feasting until his services were needed for the final battle between good and evil.

The best known version of the stories of the Germanic gods are the Old Norse *Eddas*, poems that give detailed descriptions and stories. The Anglo-Saxon versions of the stories are almost forgotten, but there is a surprising survival of the old gods in our names for the days of the week and important festivals.

Developments

Encourage the children choose one god or goddess that interests them. They could draw the outline of the figure, cut it out, and adapt it in the following ways:

- Draw in a face. This would be a wise, bearded face for Woden, a fierce face for Thunor and Tiw.
- Clothe the figures appropriately, for example a goddess would have long flowing robes and most of the gods would wear chain mail. Woden would be dressed like a king.
- Choose some accessories and copy them on to the appropriate figure.
- Colour the figure and write a brief description underneath.

- Make a large wall display of the gods and goddesses of Asgard. The backdrop could be a mountainous scene with clouds at the base of the picture. Valhalla could be drawn in the foreground. Gods and goddesses made by the children could be pasted on either side.
- Research Anglo-Saxon derivations of festivals:
  - **YULE** is the god of winter. His feast is Yuletide (changed by the early Christians to Christmas).
  - **OESTRE** is the goddess of fertility. Her festival is Easter (taken over by the early Christians).
- Make a chart for the class to fill in. They will find the information on the activity sheet. Do the same with any of the six major religions of today, and compare the results.

Name of god	Status	Objects associated with festival

Anglo-Saxon Religion

- Match the information to the correct god or goddess.

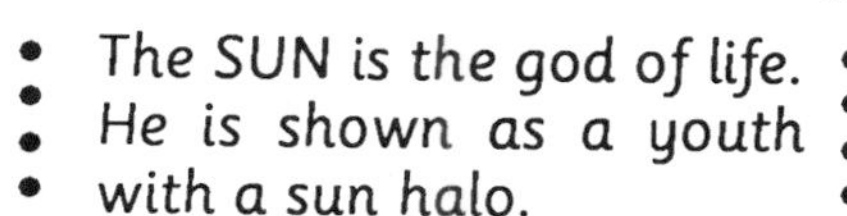

The SUN is the god of life. He is shown as a youth with a sun halo.

WODEN is the chief god, sometimes called the 'All-father'. He is dressed like a king and carries a spear to show his authority.

The MOON is the goddess of hunting. She wears a white robe and carries a bow and arrow.

THUNOR is the god of thunder. He is dressed as a warrior and carries a war hammer (with which he makes the noise of thunder) and a bolt of lightning.

TIW is the god of war. He is dressed like an Anglo-Saxon warrior and carries a battle-axe.

FREYA is the goddess of love and the wife of Woden. She carries no symbols - her beauty is enough to show what she is.

- Write which god is associated with each day.

Sunday	
Monday	
Tuesday	
Wednesday	
Thursday	
Friday	
Saturday	

SATURN is the god of fun and feasting. He is fat and jolly and is often shown eating and drinking.

The Coming of Christianity - Ideas Page

Aim

To explain some of the reasons for the conversion of the British to Christianity and to learn about Pope Gregory and St Augustine.

Preparation

- The children will need a basic knowledge of Anglo-Saxon religion (see page 18) and Christian beliefs. Therefore, the activity may need to be linked to RE work in progress.

Background

Christianity was first introduced to Britain by the Romans, but the Anglo-Saxons were pagans and this caused Christianity to disappear from large parts of Britain. Gregory, a young monk, recognised the problem when he saw Angle slave boys for sale in Rome. It was not until he became Pope that he was able to do something about it. He organised a mission, led by Augustine, to preach the Christian faith in Britain. St Augustine preached to King Ethelbert of Kent and converted him. He was then given permission to preach throughout Kent. Augustine died in AD604 and was made a saint. The story of how the other Anglo-Saxon kingdoms were converted is told in Bede's *Ecclesiastical History of the English People* (AD731), which is thought to be the first history of the English ever written.

Activity

- Working in small groups, the children should read the strip-cartoon version of the story of the conversion of the British and match the text to the correct picture.
- Ask them what they think Gregory might have said in his first sermon. Give them a structure for their answers by writing two titles, **The bad things about the Anglo-Saxon religion** and **The good things about Christianity**. Some ideas are given below.

Bad things about Anglo-Saxon religion	Good things about Christianity
Valhalla is only for warriors who die in battle.	Everybody who is good can go to heaven.
It encourages fighting.	It encourages good behaviour.
The gods are more like people than gods.	There is a philosophy of peace and love.
There are too many gods.	There is only one God.
Archaelogists have found evidence of human sacrifices to gods.	

Developments

- The children's suggestions for the two categories could be used as a basis for improvised drama:
  - Working in groups of four, one child preaches Christianity to the group, using the notes. The others are the Anglo-Saxons who ask questions about the new religion.
  - A member of the group could take the part of a village 'wise man' or 'wise woman' who speaks in favour of the old gods. When the activities are over, tell the children the end of the story. (Augustine was successful in converting the Anglo-Saxons and was made a saint.)
- Research how far Christianity spread in Anglo-Saxon Britain.

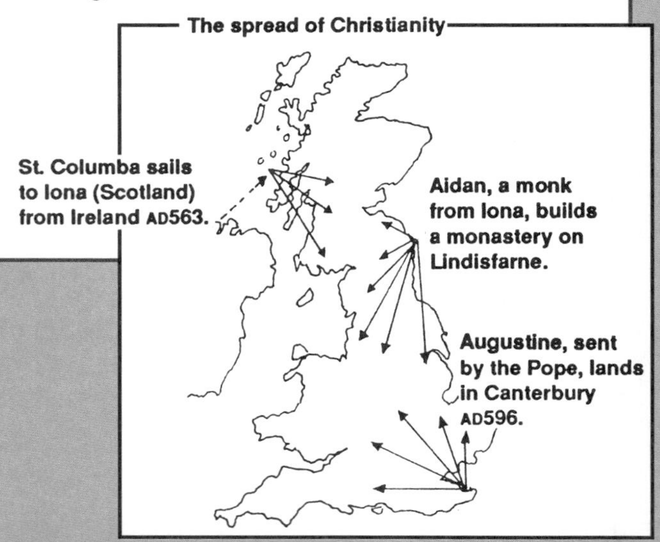

Conversion to Christianity

He admires their blond hair and asks who they are and where they are from. The merchant replies that they are pagans - Angles from the island of Britain. "That is appropriate," replies Gregory, "because they have angelic faces."

Gregory asks the Pope if he will send missionaries to convert the Angles to Christianity. He refuses.

When Gregory becomes Pope, he remembers the slaves with angelic faces - the Angles - and sends a missionary, Augustine, to convert them.

In AD597 Augustine goes to Britain and preaches his first sermon to King Ethelbert of Kent.

Gregory, a young monk, sees some young boys for sale in the slave market in Rome.

- Match the caption to the correct picture to tell the story.
- What might Augustine have written in his first sermon?

An Anglo-Saxon Church - Ideas Page

Aim

To learn to recognise some of the main features of Anglo-Saxon architecture.

Background

The first Anglo-Saxon churches were made from wood. The only surviving example can be seen at Greenstead in Essex. Later, many churches were rebuilt in stone, and though some of the features of the wooden structures were kept for decoration, such as strapwork (see below). Anglo-Saxon churches were very simple, often consisting of only a nave and a tower. The nave would often have a thatched roof. In the later middle-ages most churches were enlarged by raising the tower, adding a porch and side aisles, and adding decorative finials and ornamental windows. In many English churches the basic Anglo-Saxon structure can still be seen.

Activity

- Provide pairs of children with the following instructions to make the model:
  - Paste the activity sheet on to thin card. Cut out the templates, fold the tabs and assemble the basic shape.
  - Make a flat roof for the tower by cutting out a square of card 5.3cm by 5.3cm, plus three 1cm tabs. These should be folded and pasted.
  - Make a roof for the nave by cutting out a rectangle of card 8.5cm by 6.8cm and folding it down the middle. This is pasted to the tabs on top of the nave walls. The roof can be painted or covered with straw.
  - Paint the church to resemble stone.

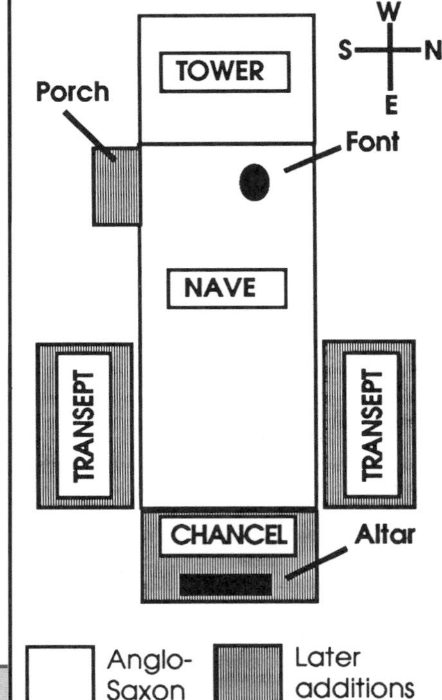

Developments

- There may be some Anglo-Saxon architecture in one of your local churches. If possible, take the children to the church and ask them to identify the features using the activity sheet.
- The children could draw and label the key features of their own Anglo-Saxon church.
- Do some class research and find out about:
  - the differences between this church and other churches
  - the internal plan of other churches.

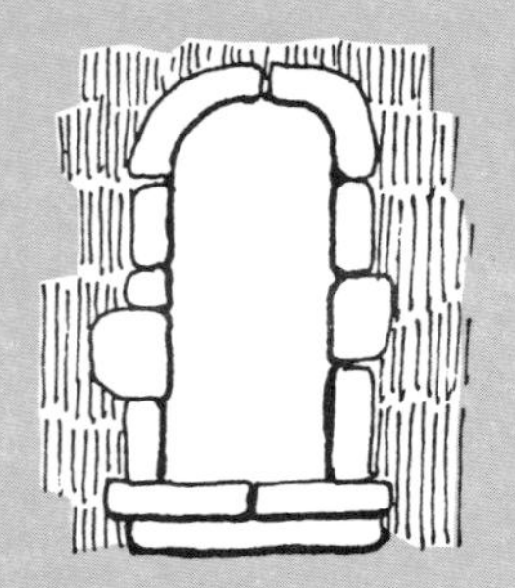

Single-arched window

Triangular windows

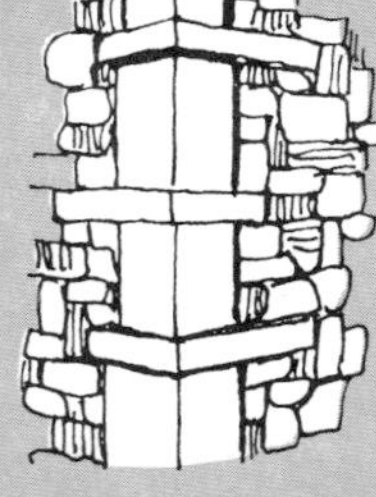

Long and short brickwork

Double-arched window with baluster

An Anglo-Saxon Church

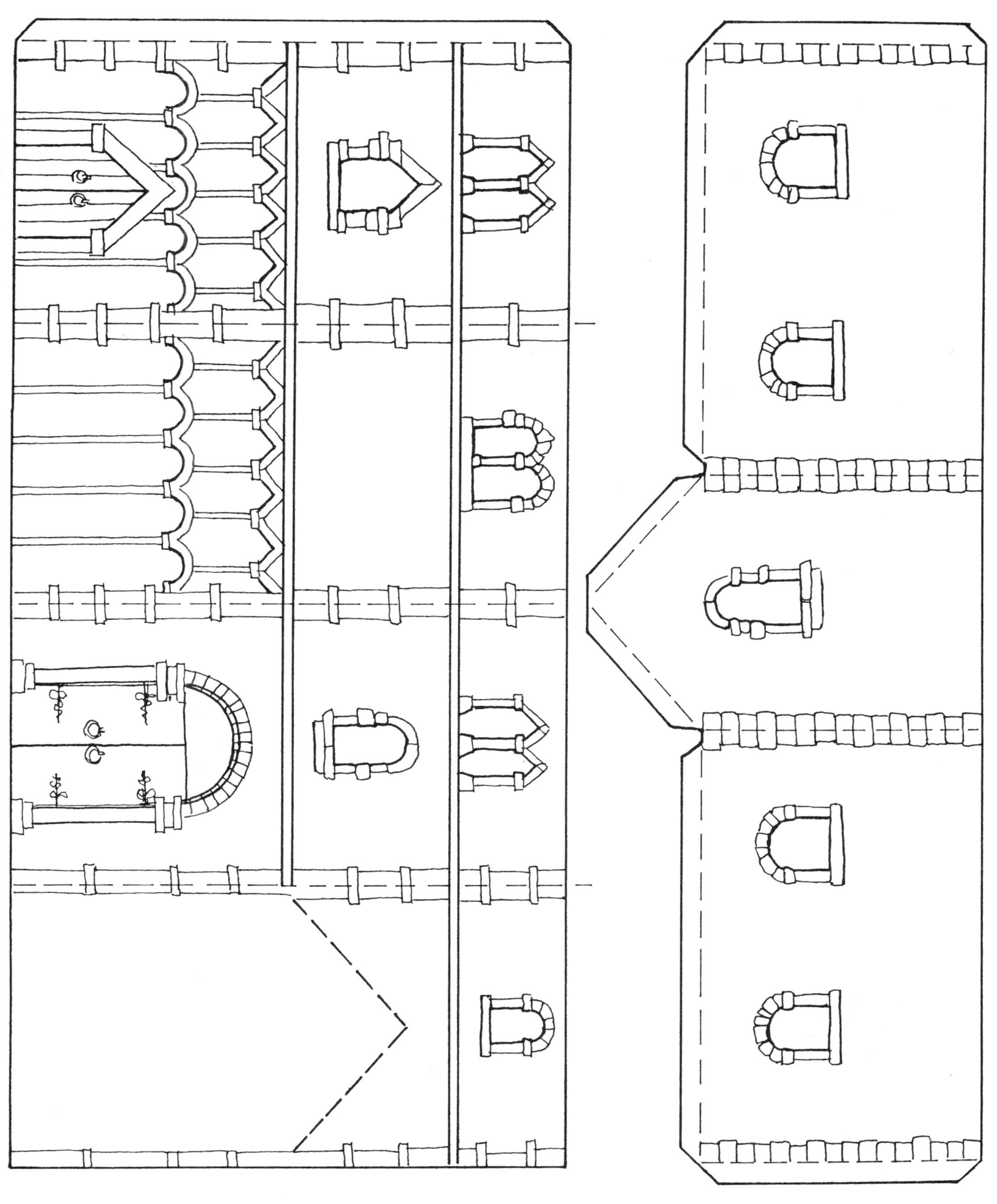

The Sutton Hoo Ship Burial - Ideas Page

Aim

For the children to learn how to make use of archaeological evidence.

Activity

- What can we tell about the person this ship burial commemorates? Use the following prompt questions to help the children to complete the activity:
  - Was the person a man or woman?
  - Was he/she rich or poor?
  - What did he/she enjoy doing?
  - Was he/she a king/queen, a farmer, a warrior, a minstrel?
- Shield ornaments have also been found. The shield had rotted away so no-one knows exactly how the ornaments were arranged. Ask the children to draw a circle 10cm across, cut out or draw the ornaments and experiment to find their best position (note that the shield boss must always be in the centre). When the best position has been found, paste and colour them.

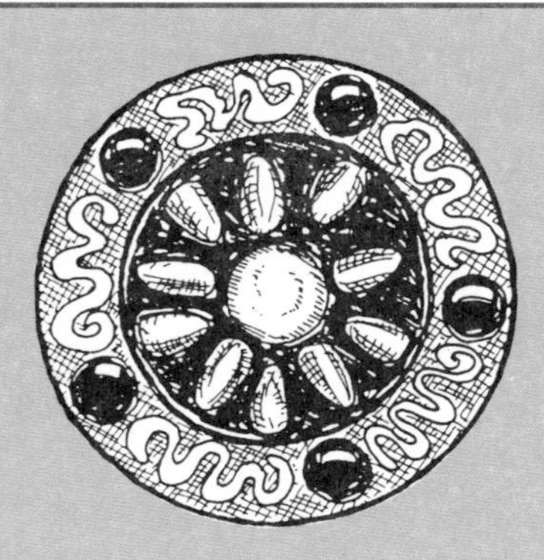

Background

Archaeological evidence can help build up a picture of Anglo-Saxon life. One of the richest finds was made in 1939 at Sutton Hoo near Woodbridge in Suffolk. At some time in the seventh century, a whole ship, filled with objects, had been buried in memory of an important ruler. The ship itself had completely rotted way, but archaeologists were able to work out its size and shape from the rivets which had held it together. It is not known which ruler the burial commemorated, but King Raedwald has been suggested as a possibility.

Developments

- Give the children a list of other items found in the ship: buckles, brooches, lyre, sword, helmet, drinking horns, purse, spears. Ask them to look for pictures or drawings of these in library books.
- Fill a suitcase with a selection of objects belonging to an imaginary person. The objects are 'evidence' which the children can use to build up a picture of the owner.
- This extract from *Beowulf* describes an Anglo-Saxon burial:

There in the harbour, stood the ice prowed ship,
the prince's vessel, shrouded in ice and
eager to sail;
and they laid their dear lord,
the giver of rings, deep within the ship,
by the mast in the majesty; many treasures
and adornments from far and wide were
gathered there.

- The extract could be the basis for story writing, with the children describing the burial of the Sutton Hoo ship and its owner.

The Sutton Hoo Ship Burial

- Look at some of the remains found at Sutton Hoo:

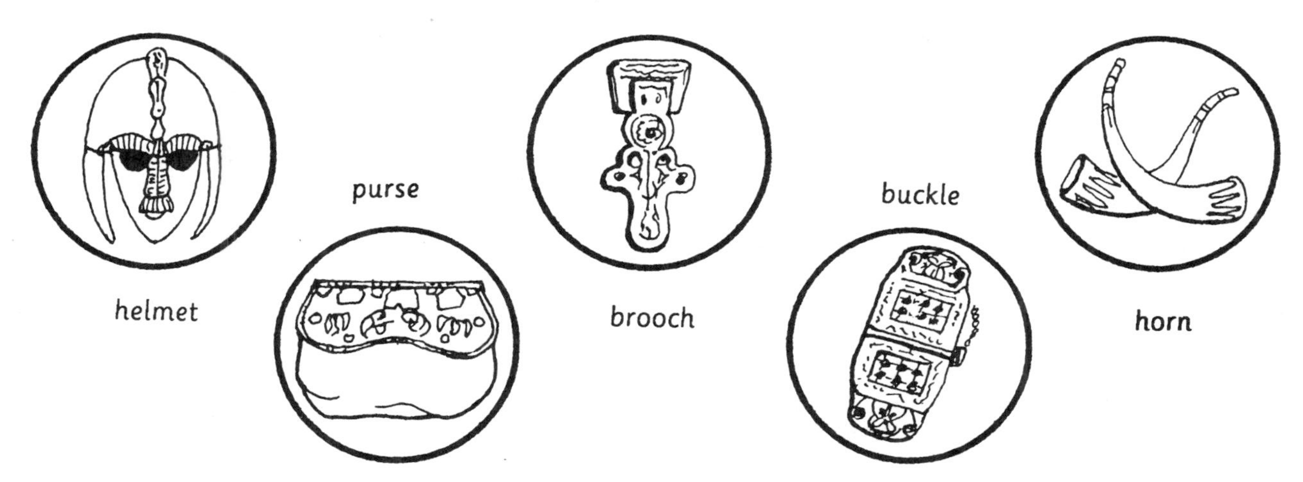

- What sort of person might have been buried here? Complete the chart below.

The evidence	My conclusion	What I need to find out
The helmet	A warrior, not a woman	Did women fight in wars?

- Design a shield, using the shield ornaments below. Put the shield boss in the middle.

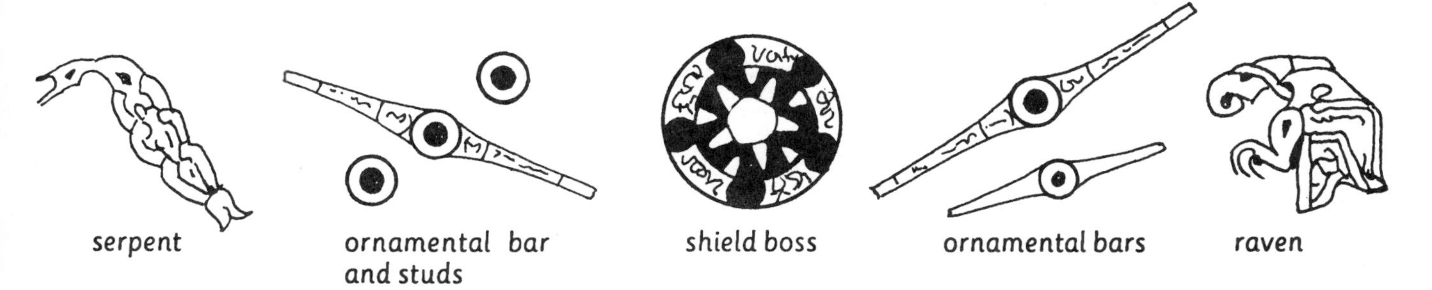

Arms and Armour - Ideas Page

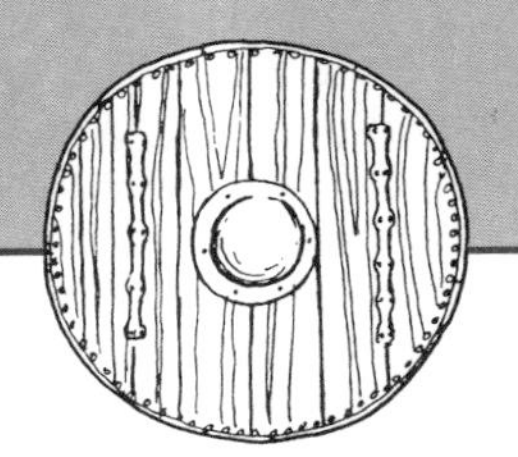

Aim

To learn about the arms and armour of Anglo-Saxon warriors.

Activity

- The children should consider what arms and armour would have been most suitable for an Anglo-Saxon warrior and why.
- What weapons will the children give the warrior? They could put one in his hand and one in his belt.

Background

Grave finds show that most Anglo-Saxon warriors would have been equipped with a knife, a spear and a shield. Only a few could afford expensive items such as helmets, mail shirts and swords. Several types of helmet have been found, ranging from a round metal cap with a boar crest, to the elaborately decorated Sutton Hoo helmet. The most recent find, at Jorvik, York, has a 'nasal' to protect the face and a chain mail 'aventail' to protect the neck.

Mail shirts were made up of thousands of rings interlinked and rivetted by hand. The amount of workmanship involved must have made them very expensive.

The style of armour changed throughout the Anglo-Saxon period. By 1066 it was similar to that worn by the Normans, such as a heavy 'hauberk' of chain mail and a conical helmet with a nasal. There were some small differences. Anglo-Saxons preferred to fight on foot using a round shield and a battle axe. Normans, who fought on horseback, developed a kite-shaped shield to help protect the legs.

Developments

- The children could cut out the figure of the warrior and paste on a suitable outfit. All the drawings are based on archaeological finds and the task recreates the process archaeologists go through to reconstruct the past.
- No complete mail shirts have been found, only small pieces of interlinked rings, so we are not sure what mail shirts looked like. The children could make them long (as in the picture) or short, and they could have long or short sleeves.
- Many ornate brooches and buckles have been found. Brooches were used to fasten cloaks and buckles to fasten belts. The warrior would probably have worn a cloak, so the children could draw in an appropriate ornamental brooch to fasten it.
- Make an Anglo-Saxon army display:
  - Collect together all the finished cut-outs and paste them on to a large sheet of paper to make an Anglo-Saxon army.
  - Some children could draw the ships in the background and add figures in different postures.
- The children could use the figure on the activity sheet to help them draw a modern soldier with all his kit and weapons.
- Discuss the similarities and differences between soldiers then and soldiers today. Discuss why this might be.

	Anglo-Saxons	Today	Reasons for difference
Clothes			
Weapons			

Anglo-Saxon soldiers

Arms and Armour

- Choose some clothes and weapons for this warrior and explain why you chose them.

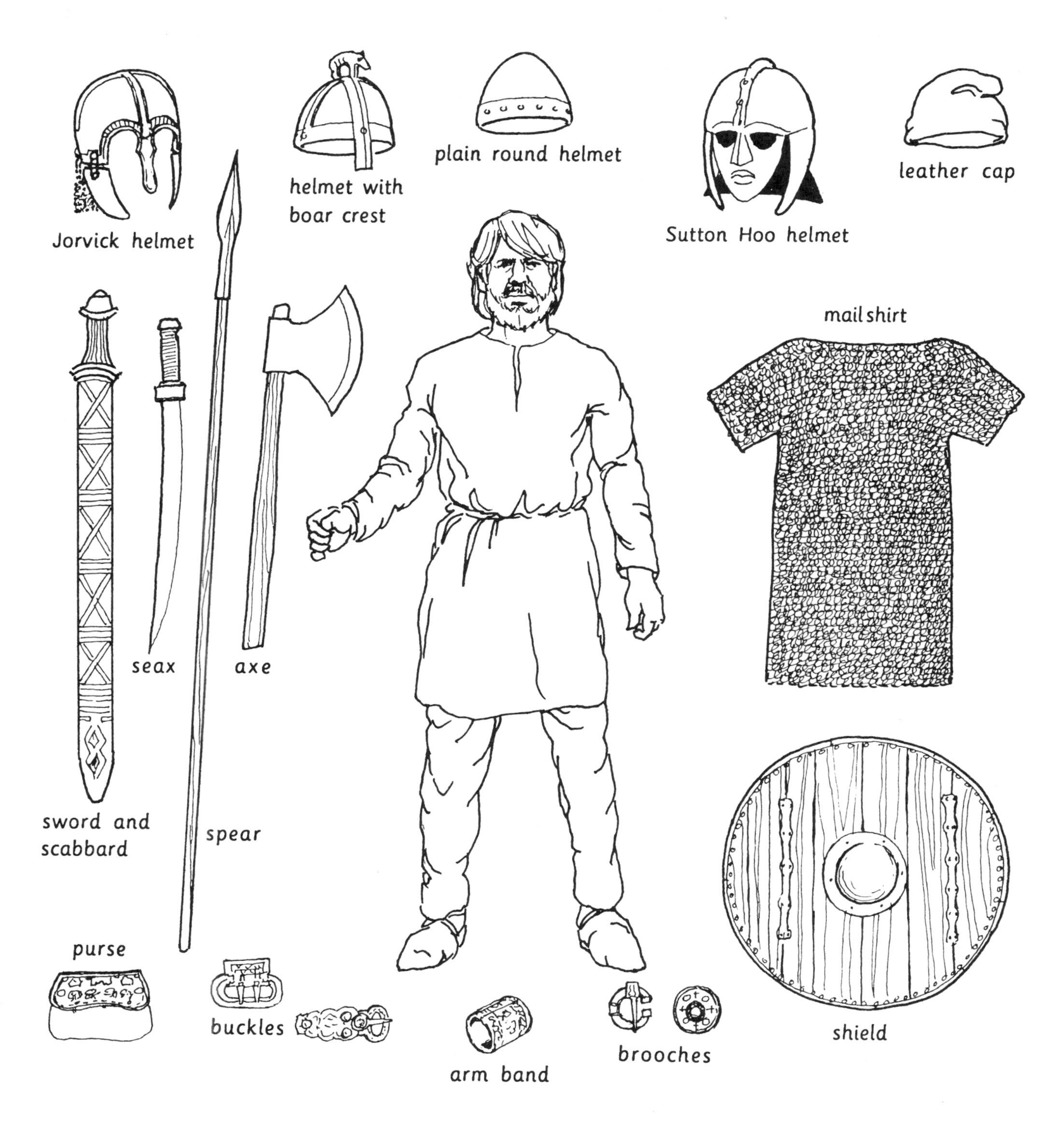

- What would he use to attack an enemy?
- What would help to protect him?

Women - Ideas Page

Aim

To learn something about women in Anglo-Saxon society and to consider the interpretation of sources.

Background

The evidence of wills and place names shows that rich Anglo-Saxon women often held large estates and were the equal of their husbands and brothers in terms of power. However, for the peasant woman, life was a continual round of cooking, cleaning, weaving and needlework.

WEALTHEOW: In the poem *Beowulf* the Danish queen, Wealtheow, has an important part to play. She makes a speech in praise of Beowulf's heroic deeds and gives him a gift of treasure. Later, she and her daughter Freawaru serve the ale-cup to each of the courtiers in turn - not as servants, but as hosts. Both of these actions are indications of their status.

ABBESS HILD: Hild was born into the royal house of Northumbria and became a nun at the age of 33. She founded a new abbey at Whitby and built up its reputation until it became famous as a centre of learning. Her wisdom was so great that kings and leaders from all over Britain came to her for advice.

AETHELFLAED: Aethelflaed was the eldest child of Alfred the Great. She married elderman Aethelred, ruler of Mercia. After her husband's death she ruled Mercia for seven years. She led battles against the Vikings and the Welsh, and built a chain of ten fortresses to protect Mercia against the Danes of the Danelaw.

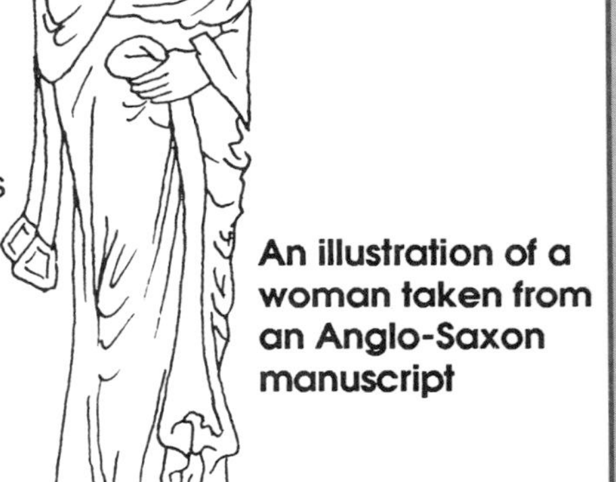

An illustration of a woman taken from an Anglo-Saxon manuscript

Activity

- The activity sheet shows how Anglo-Saxon women have been interpreted in the past - from the romantic versions of Camelot to contemporary art (such as the drawing of the statue of Abbess Hild). Ask the children to discuss what impressions of women each picture gives.
- Ask them to draw a picture of a woman they know, perhaps a politician or a teacher, clearly showing the style of dress.
- Challenge the children to use reference books to find out how both rich and poor Anglo-Saxon women lived and dressed. Compare the findings and list any differences.
- Give children information to show how much power Anglo-Saxon women could have. Are they surprised? Why?

Developments

- Ask the children to choose one of the women described above and draw a picture of her. She should be given appropriate clothes and artefacts, which the children will have to research. For example, Hild would wear a nun's habit, Aethelflaed would dress simply, but would wear some items worn by a male warrior.
- Make a wall display of the figures, with a brief description of their lives and achievements underneath.
- This picture shows girdle hangers. Archaeologists have not been able to find out what they were used for. Ask the children for some suggestions.

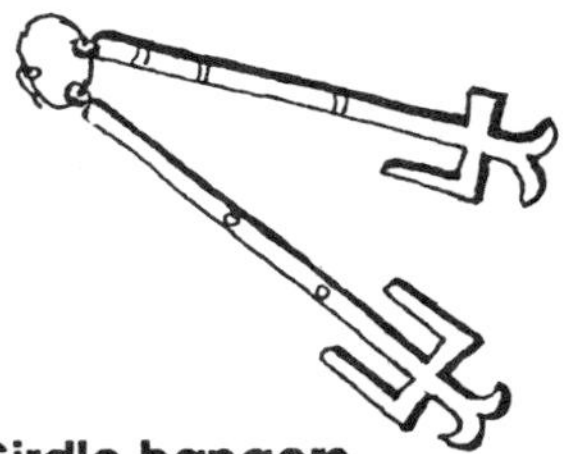

Girdle hangers

Women

Picture A is a drawing of a ninth-century statue of an Anglo-Saxon woman (Saint Hild). Picture B is a drawing of Lady Godiva from a history book.

A

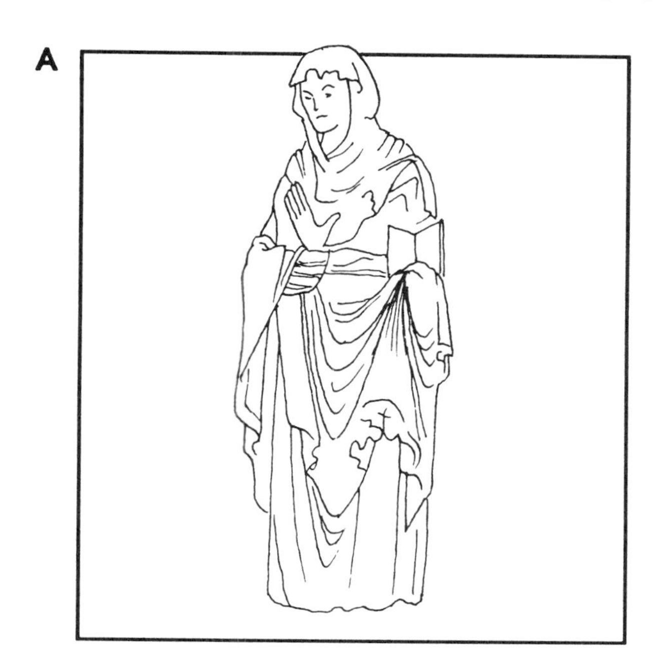

B

- Find out how Anglo-Saxon women dressed. Which drawing is right?
  - Draw a woman you know. How is she dressed?
  - Draw a modern princess. How is she dressed?

- Find out about Aethelflaed, King Alfred's daughter, and about an ordinary Anglo-Saxon woman. How are they different from the pictures you have drawn?

An Anglo-Saxon Village - Ideas Page

Aim

To learn about the lay-out and structure of Anglo-Saxon villages.

Activity

- Ask the children to look at and discuss the features of the Anglo-Saxon village on the activity sheet.
  - What can they see?
  - How does this differ from a small country village today?
  - What would be the same?
- Discuss the location of the village next to a water supply and the importance of the church to village life. The power of the lord should be obvious by the size and location of the lord's hall.

Background

The Anglo-Saxon invaders ignored the crumbling Romano-British cities and created settlements of their own. They preferred to live in small villages which were largely self-sufficient.

A typical Anglo-Saxon village would be situated on fertile land near a stream or river. There would be at least three large fields to allow for crop rotation. A typical rotation was oats, barley, fallow. Every villager would have a number of strips in each field. There would also be an area of common land which everyone could use to graze their cattle.

Houses were simple wattle-and-daub huts - often grouped around a 'moot place', a meeting place where villagers could meet to discuss their affairs. The only large buildings would be the lord's hall and the church, and these would be built from wood. In the latter part of the Anglo-Saxon period many churches were rebuilt in stone.

Developments

- Archaelogists re-building the Anglo-Saxon village at West Stow in Suffolk had to consider:
  - what materials were used to build the original houses
  - what shape and size the original houses were.

  The children could talk about how they might find out this information.
- Make a model of the Anglo-Saxon village. Groups of children could research the layout of an Anglo-Saxon village and what we know of the houses they lived in.
  - Collect modelling materials (cardboard, straws, lollipop sticks, twigs, straw, sand). Railway modelling materials, such as small trees, miniature people and farm animals can be useful.
  - One group could make a lord's hall.
  - Another group could make the church (see pages 22 and 23).
- The children could think of a name for their village, including an element of an Anglo-Saxon place-name (see page 36). They could also:
  - think of a name for each family
  - divide the fields up into strips and give each family a strip in each field. The lord should have two strips in each field.
  - draw an accurate map of the village.
- Ask the children to research and discuss what they think life would be like in such a village. They could record their findings under headings such as: availability of water, diet, health, hygiene, power and hours of work.

Anglo-Saxon buildings

An Anglo-Saxon Village

Look carefully at this picture of an Anglo-Saxon village.

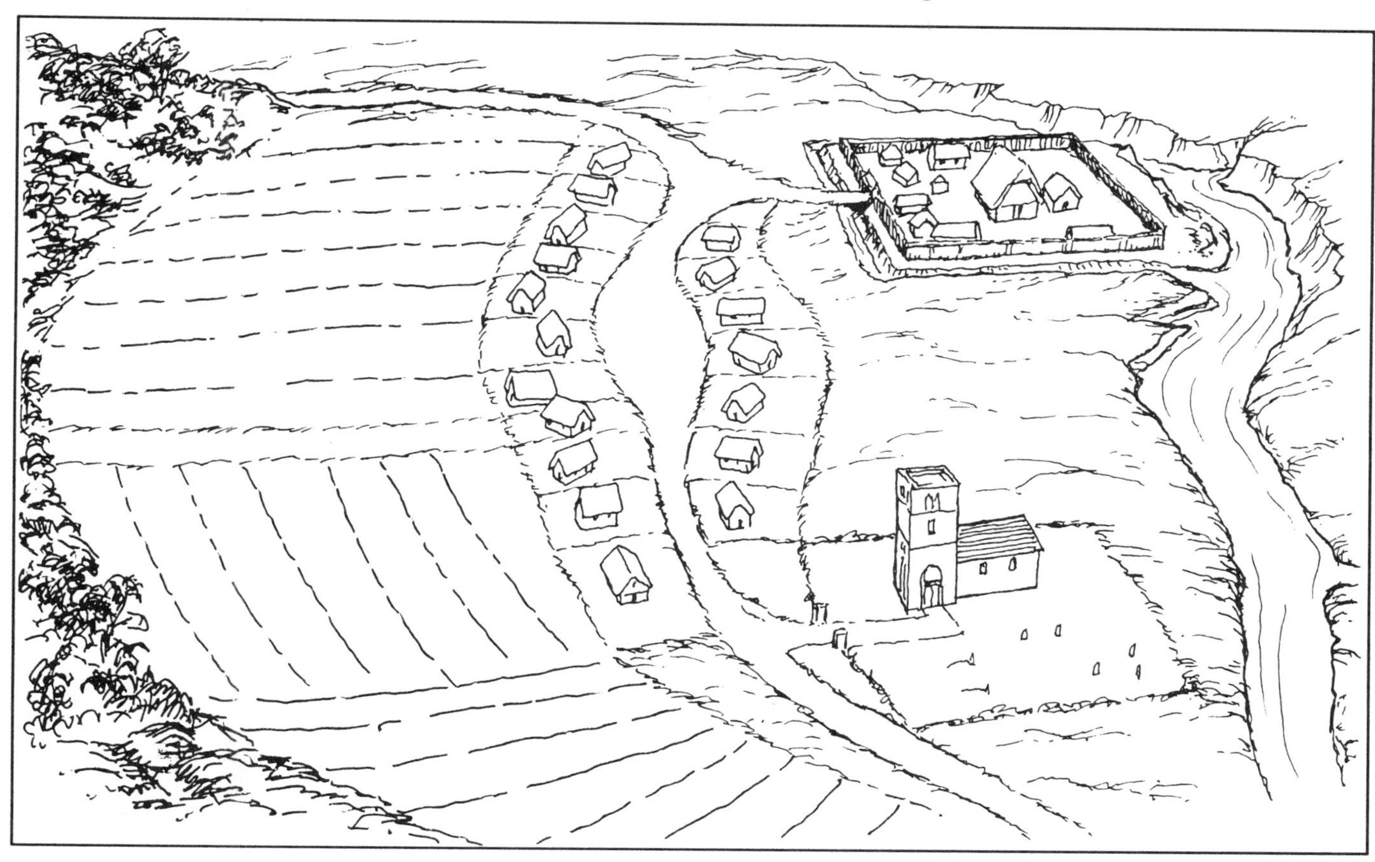

- Label the strip fields, the church and the lord's hall.
- What are the most important buildings? How do you know?
- Why do you think the Saxons chose this location?
- In what ways is this different from a village today?

Anglo-Saxon Village	Modern Village

A Farmer's Year - Ideas Page

Aim

To find out about everyday life in Anglo-Saxon Britain, using the Burnham Deepdale font as evidence.

Activity

- In pairs, the children should examine each picture and discuss what the farmer is doing.
- Initiate a class discussion, encouraging different interpretations of the pictures.

Background

Everyday life in Anglo-Saxon times revolved around the village and the farm. Two of the best sources of evidence for this are the *Anglo-Saxon Calendar* and the carvings on the font in the church at Burnham Deepdale, Norfolk. The font shows a scene for each month in a typical farmer's year.

In the winter there was not much to do, so in January and February he would drink and sit in front of the fire. March shows him digging; he would probably have done further preparation by ploughing the field. In April he is seen pruning his fruit trees. In May he appears to be 'beating the bounds' - marching around his fields with a banner to drive off evil spirits. In June he weeds the crops. The scenes for July, August and September show the process of harvesting - cutting wheat with a scythe, bundling the sheaves and threshing. In October he grinds corn with a stone quern. In November he kills a pig and in December he enjoys a feast with his family and friends.

Developments

- After deciding what the farmer is doing every month, the children could draw a circular farm calendar to show the Anglo-Saxon farmer's year.
- The children could research a modern farmer's year and discuss the differences. Why does a modern farmer not find it necessary to drive off evil spirits from his land? What did the Anglo-Saxons think these spirits were responsible for? Does a modern farmer have similar problems? How would he or she deal with them?
- Children could identify the tools in the pictures and make a chart, as in **A**.
- Bring together the work on villages (see pages 30-31) and the calendar. Use it as the basis for drama and a discussion of causes and consequences.
  - Name the farmer on the font. Choose a house in the Anglo-Saxon village where he could live.
  - Invent his family group.
  - Talk about the problems he may face. List the various points and use it as a basis for planning, as in **B**.

A

Then	Now	Use	Differences	Why?
Scythe	*Harvester*	*Cutting crops*	*A machine now*	*Technology has developed*

B

Problem	Cause	Consequences	Drama points
Bad harvest	*Bad weather* *Disease*	*Family cannot feed itself* *Cannot pay tythe to Lord* *No corn to plant next year.*	*?*

A Farmer's Year

Medicine - Ideas Page

Aim

To provide the children with an insight into Anglo-Saxon medicine and to compare Anglo-Saxon health with our own.

Background

The word 'leech' meant doctor, and was used as a slang word for doctor until recently. This was because of the common practice of placing leeches on a patient in the belief that they would suck out the illness as they sucked blood.

Anglo-Saxon 'doctors' used a mixture of herbal remedies and magic. They could even offer a spell to help find something, or a potion to make someone fall in love with you!

Activity

- The children work in pairs to read out the remedies from Bald's Leechbook.
- Discuss how effective each remedy might be.
- Answer the question in the 'Modern' column.

Developments

- The children could write their own Leechbook. They could do this by asking relatives about any traditional herbal cures they know of.
- The children could work in pairs or small groups to produce a page for a class Leechbook. These pages could be partly in runes (pages 38-39) and decorated with Anglo-Saxon motifs (pages 46-47).
- There is a poetic element to the remedies in their strange-sounding plant names and the strange rituals that go into the preparation. Ask the children to write their own remedies or spells in poetic form, perhaps using the index of a botanical text to find unusual and magical sounding plant names.
- Ask the children to research and make a comparison chart using the following facts and statistics.

Anglo-Saxon health	Modern health	Reasons for changes
Average height of men: 174cm Average height of women: 156cm Average age at death (men): 40 Average age at death (women): 35 1 in 3 children died before the age of 10 ***Common illnesses:*** arthritis fractures (particularly of the leg and wrist) plague malnutrition (tooth decay was rare)		

- Ask the children to carry out their own research. For example, they could find out the heights of teachers and parents and work out the averages. The most common illness could then be decided by class discussion.
- How do the children think that information about Anglo-Saxon health has been discovered?

Anglo-Saxon Remedies

In the eighth century, a leech ('leech' is the Anglo-Saxon word for 'doctor') called Bald wrote down some of his favourite remedies.

- *Compare them with remedies used today and complete the chart below.*

	BALD'S LEECHBOOK	TODAY
FOR A HEADACHE	Look for little stones in the stomachs of swallows' chicks. Take care that they do not touch earth or water or other stones. Sew up three of them in a bag and place it on the head.	What would we use to cure a headache today?
TO CURE A BEE STING	Take dead bees and burn them to ashes. Add oil, pound willow leaves, and boil over the coals. Strain the mixture and rub it into the sting.	What would we use to cure a bee sting today?
PROTECTION AGAINST ELVES AND GOBLINS	Take hop-plant, wormwood, betony, lupin, vervain, henbane, dittander, viper's bugloss, bilberry plants, cropleek, garlic, madder grains, corn cockle, fennel. Put the plants in a vat, place the vat under an altar and sing nine masses over it. Boil in butter and sheep's grease. Rub on the face of the person you wish to protect.	What would your doctor say if you asked him for some medicine to protect you against elves and goblins?
PROTECTION AGAINST GOSSIP	Eat nothing all day, then eat a radish at night. That day the gossip cannot harm you.	If you wanted to protect yourself against gossip, how would you do it?

Language - Ideas Page

Aim

For the children to explore the relationship between Anglo-Saxon and modern English.

Background

Anglo-Saxon, or Old English, is so different from modern English because of the influences of the languages of invaders and settlers, particularly the Vikings and the Normans. Indeed, Anglo-Saxon is so different from modern English that it has to be learned like a foreign language. However, its relationship to modern English can be seen.

Although many words are the same or very similar, they are often disguised by different spellings, different vowel sounds and different grammatical affixes (plurals other than -s). The four examples given on the activity sheet can be used to show children how to guess words by reading aloud and trying different versions of the vowel sound (longer, rounder, and so on).

Anglo-Saxon scripts use four letters not used in the modern alphabet. The two commonest are given on the activity sheet. Thorn was borrowed from the Anglo-Saxon runic alphabet and is interesting in that it is a pictogram (like Egyptian hieroglyphs or Chinese characters). It is a simplified picture of a thorn on a branch.

Activity

fisc fish	**eorl** earl	**mann** man	**Breten** Britain	**lytel** little
norp north	**mup** mouth	**freond** friend	**meolc** milk	**pusend** thousand
sweord sword	**woruld** world	**wyrm** worm	**hus** house	**beginnan** begin
her here	**cyning** king	**daeg** day	**stan** stone	**seofon** seven
spadu spade	**lufu** love	**sweoster** sister	**iegland** island	**wundorlic** wonderful

- Working in pairs, the children could match up the two sets of words.
- Some children might be given the set of Anglo-Saxon words and asked to guess what they mean.

Developments

- The Anglo-Saxon language is the basis for many of the place names in Britain. Show children a copy of this chart.

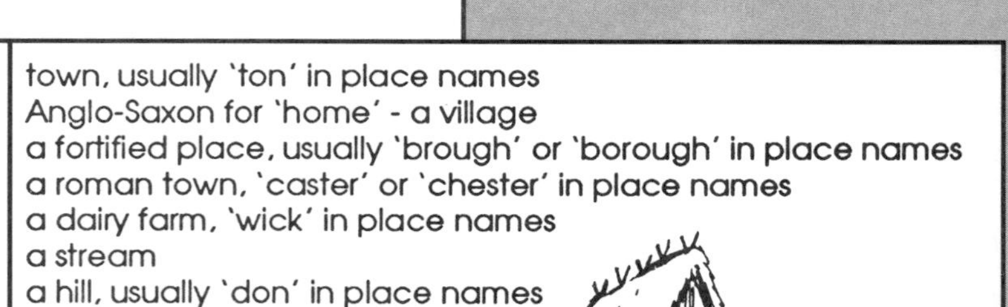

tun	town, usually 'ton' in place names
ham	Anglo-Saxon for 'home' - a village
burg	a fortified place, usually 'brough' or 'borough' in place names
ceastre	a roman town, 'caster' or 'chester' in place names
wic	a dairy farm, 'wick' in place names
burn	a stream
dun	a hill, usually 'don' in place names

- Ask them to find some of these place endings on a large-scale map of any English county.
- Read an extract from *Beowulf* (see page 40) and make an Anglo-Saxon dictionary. Identify similarities and differences in the two versions of the English language over time.
- Research the derivation of surnames. Old English has both masculine and feminine nouns for baker: *baecere* and *baecester*. These have survived as the occupational surnames Baker and Baxter. What do Brewsters, Malsters and Tapsters do?
- What does the survival of these occupational surnames with their female endings tell us about the work roles of women in Anglo-Saxon times?

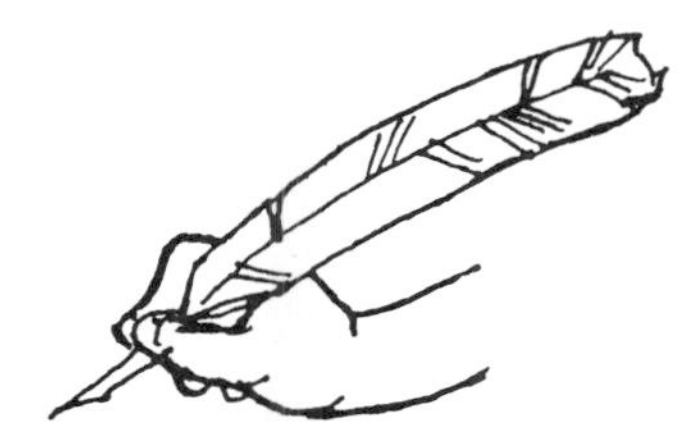

Language

Some words are the same as modern English:

gold full lamb horn land

Some are nearly the same:

fyr - fire loc - lock beor - beer blod - blood

Anglo-Saxon uses extra letters:

ȝ is called 'ash' and sounds like 'a' in 'ash'
þ is called 'thorn' and sounds like 'th' in 'thorn'.

- Cut out and match the Anglo-Saxon words to the modern English ones.

fisc	eorl	mann	Breten	lytel
norp	mup	freond	meolc	pusend
sweord	woruld	wyrm	hus	beginnan
her	cyning	daeg	stan	seofon
spadu	lufu	sweoster	iegland	wundorlic

here	spade	sword	fish	north
love	earl	mouth	king	world
sister	worm	day	friend	man
Britain	milk	island	house	stone
wonderful	seven	begin	thousand	little

Runes - Ideas Page

Aim

To experiment with an Anglo-Saxon writing system.

Background

Runes were a special form of writing used throughout the Germanic tribes. They are a simplified version of the Roman alphabet, consisting of mainly straight lines. This makes them suitable for carving on wood, stone and metal.

Runes were thought to have a magical significance. This can easily be understood if we remember how few people at that time could read and write.

Activity

- The rune cards provide an opportunity for the children to explore runes for both writing and fortune telling.
- Ask the children to write their names using runes. This is quite simple, apart from remembering to use 'double letter' runes: 'th', 'qu' and 'st, c/k and i/j use the same rune.
- They could write to each other or use runes for titles when writing about Anglo-Saxons.

Developments

- To make the runes more authentic, collect twenty-four smooth pebbles of about 2-3cm in size and paint the runes on them. Play the game again using these.
- The written word has changed a great deal over time.
  - Why was there no writing at this time as we know it?
  - Why were there no books as we know them?
- The picture below shows a section from the Franks Casket in the British Museum. It is carved in ivory:
  - Read the runes on the picture ('MAGI').
  - What does this tell us about the scene on the casket?
  - What does this tell us about the religion of the casket's owner?

- Before using the cards for fortune telling, it is important to check that none of your children or their parents would find this activity unacceptable for religious reasons. The children cut out the cards and use them to form the letters of the name of the person whose fortune is to be told (two or more sets may be needed!).
- Alternatively, the cards can be shuffled and seven selected at random by the person whose fortune is to be told.
  - The fortune teller then looks at the different meanings and tries to piece them together.
  - Tell the children they should use what they already know about the person to help them.
  - They should not try to use every card, leaving out any that seem to contradict all the rest.

Runes

Rune	Name and Meaning	Letter	Rune	Name and Meaning	Letter	Rune	Name and Meaning	Letter
	Wealth *You will inherit some money*	F		**Hail** *You have a problem*	H		**A horse** *Someone will help you*	E
	A wild ox *You will be brave and strong*	U		**Need** *You will suffer hunger or thirst*	N		**Man** *An important person will come into your life*	M
	Thorn *You must face trouble and pain*	TH		**Ice** *You will suffer sorrow or loneliness*	I J		**A lake** *You will enjoy a time of peace and relaxation*	L
	The god, Os *Some good luck is coming your way*	O		**A pawn** *Someone is bullying you*	P		**A day** *Do not waste your life!*	D
	Riding *You are going on a journey*	R		**A reed** *You give in too easily*	X		**An oak tree** *You will be strong and steadfast*	A
	A pine torch *You will find out a secret*	C K		**The sun** *You will be fortunate, happy and successful*	S		**A bow** *You must have clear aims in life*	Y
	A gift *You will receive a gift soon*	G		**The god, Tir** *You want something badly and soon you will get it*	T		**Love** *Someone loves you*	QU
	Joy *You will hear some good news*	W		**A birch tree** *You will be punished for something you have done wrong*	B		**A stone** *A disappointment awaits you*	ST

Beowulf - Ideas Page

Aim

To introduce the children to the greatest surviving example of Anglo-Saxon literature.

Activity

- The cards on the activity sheet show eight key scenes from the poem, each with a brief description. Working in pairs, the children could place the cards in the correct order and talk about what makes the story exciting.

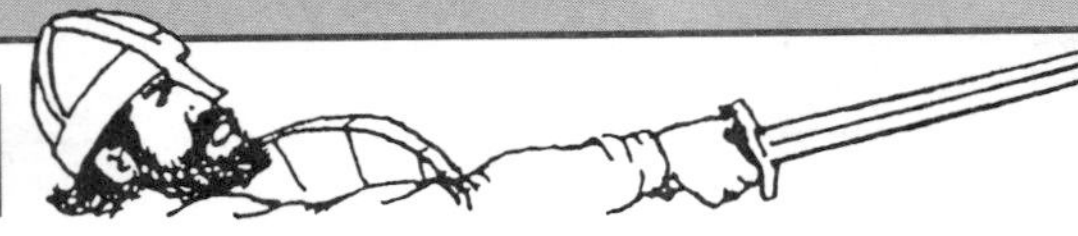

Background

Beowulf is the oldest surviving epic poem in any Germanic language. It was written down in the eighth century, but was composed orally and passed on by word of mouth for hundreds of years. The poem is set in the Germanic homeland of Denmark and 'Geatland' - part of Sweden. It is partly mythological and partly historical - many names and places appear in the historical record.

We can learn a great deal about Anglo-Saxon culture from the poem, particularly about the 'heroic code' of loyalty to one's leader and bravery in battle.

However, its value is more than antiquarian - it is a good story in its own right. Over a hundred translations have been made, several for children. One translation for the junior age range is *Dragon Slayer* by Rosemary Sutcliffe.

The poem has an interesting alliteration and verse form - each line had four stresses emphasised by alliterating words.

This was the manner of the mourning of the men of the Geats,
Sharers in the feast, at the fall of their lord:
They said that he was of all the world's kings
The gentlest of men, and the most gracious,
The kindest to his people, the keenest for fame.

Developments

- The children could work in groups of four to produce a detailed written version of *Beowulf*. Give each child two scenes to develop. They could discuss each other's work and finally edit it together to form a longer story. This could be presented in booklet form with illustrations.
- Ask groups of children to write alliterative poetry, perhaps even using four stresses in a line.
  - Illustrate 'stress' in poetry by using a simple poetic form such as a limerick.
  - Illustrate 'alliteration' by using simple tongue-twisters.
- Provide groups of children with a copy of some lines of the original *Beowulf* and a translation. Ask them to identify the similarities and differences between Anglo-Saxon and modern words.

Da com of more under misthleopum

Then coming of the moor under the misty slopes

Grendel gongan; Godes yrre baer;

Grendel goes/comes; God's anger he bears/carries;

Mynte se manscade manna cynnes

intends this evil monster mankind/human

sumne besyrwan in sele pam heam

someone to trap/ensnare in this noble hall.

Beowulf

Hrothgar, King of the Danes, builds a magnificent mead hall called Heorot...

...but Grendel, a marsh-dwelling troll, raids the hall every night and kills one of Hrothgar's men.

Beowulf, a prince of the Geats, sets out with fourteen followers to help Hrothgar.

Beowulf waits for Grendel in the hall. Grendel bursts in and eats a warrior. Beowulf fights him and tears off an arm. Grendel is mortally wounded.

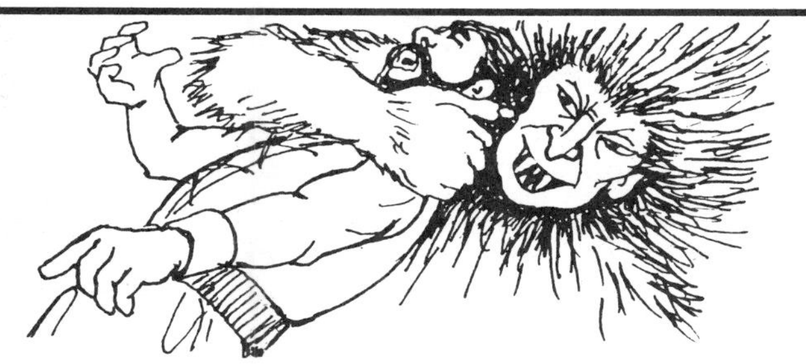

Next night an even fiercer troll, Grendel's mother, comes seeking revenge. She seizes Aschere and drags him to her lair in the swamp.

Beowulf dives down after her and fights her in the depths of the swamp. His own sword breaks, but he finds an ancient and magical blade and cuts off her head.

There is great feasting. Beowulf goes back to Geatland and becomes king. His people enjoy fifty years of peace, but the day comes when this is broken by a fierce, fire-breathing dragon.

Beowulf is old, but no-one else will face the dragon. With only one young man, Wiglafto to help him, he fights the dragon. He kills it, but is mortally wounded in the fight. He dies with great honour and is mourned by all his people.

Hall Joys - Ideas Page

Aim

To learn how Anglo-Saxons spent their leisure time and try out some Anglo-Saxon riddles.

Activity

- In pairs, the children should look carefully at the picture and describe what they can see.
  - Look at the lyre. How many strings does it have? What do they think it would sound like?
  - What kinds of food can they see. What are people eating with?
- The children could read out the Anglo-Saxon riddles and try to guess them. The answers are: shield, sun and moon and bow.
- They could then write their own Anglo-Saxon riddles. Many Anglo-Saxon riddles make the object speak for itself. Another common form was to begin with the line:

  I saw a strange creature

  and to describe something ordinary in an unusual way.

Background

The ideal of Anglo-Saxon relaxation was 'joys of life in the hall'. This could be enjoyed at every level, from the lord in his hall sitting at the high table, to the farmer in his house with his family and servants and monks sharing a meal in a monastery.

Hall joys included the following:

- Food and drink - a pleasure not to be underestimated in an age when food could go short.
- A scop (minstrel) singing, or telling a saga such as *Beowulf.*
- Boasting. Warriors were expected to boast about their loyalty to their lord - but they were expected to live up to their boasts in battle!
- Humbler folk, who could not afford a professional scop, would make their own entertainment by singing songs and asking riddles.

Developments

- Ask the children to imagine that they have to spend a night in a lonely hut with no entertainment except what they can make themselves. What stories, poems and jokes would they tell? They could role-play the situation.
- Archaeologists have discovered a Saxon settlement in Sussex. They found the food remains listed below. What do these tell us about the diet of the Anglo-Saxons?

  pig bones, sheep bones, goat bones, cattle bones, fish bones, deer bones, goose bones, seeds from wild fruit, peas, barley and wheat.

  - Would they have used cutlery to eat these types of food?
  - How would food have been cooked?
  - What would they drink out of?
- A list of goods for a feast for the King of Wessex has been found:

10 geese	20 chicken
2 oxen	10 cheeses
42 casks of ale	5 salmon
300 loaves	20 pounds of hay
10 jars of honey	

  - What sort of dishes might there have been at a feast?
  - How many people might have attended this feast?
  - What might the honey have been used for?
  - What might the hay have been used for?

Hall Joys

- Look carefully at the picture and talk about how you think Anglo-Saxons spent their leisure time.

Three Riddles

- Read these riddles aloud and try to guess them.

I am scarred by the spear
wounded by the sword
weary of battle.
I often see war
and face deadly enemies
yet no-one helps or heals me.

Answer

I saw a strange creature
a golden ship of the air
sailing across heaven.
When she had gone her way
another creature appeared,
a silver ship sailing a black sea.
No-one knows where those creatures went.

Answer

Wob is my name if you work it out.
I'm a fair creature fashioned for battle
When I bend I shoot a deadly shaft
From my stomach, I desire only to send
That deadly dart as far away as possible.

Answer

Anglo-Saxon Ornaments - Ideas Page

Aim

To learn about Anglo-Saxon ornaments through examination of artefacts and experimentation with basic patterns.

Activity

- Working in pairs, the children should study each object on the activity sheet:
  The Strickland brooch.
  How many animals can the children count? What do they think they are?
  The Sutton Hoo buckle.
  Can the children find two gripping beast heads? Follow each beast to see how it is worked into the pattern.
  The Sutton Hoo shield ornament.
  Can they find the dragon's eye, mouth and teeth?

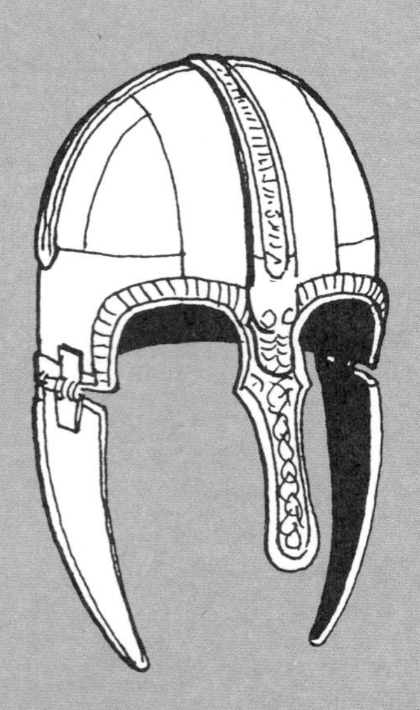

The Jorvik helmet

Background

The Anglo-Saxons loved ornamentation, which can be seen in the delicate interweaving designs and the use of coloured enamels and gems. Many of the designs are part of the common Germanic heritage, for example 'the gripping beast' motif can be found in England and throughout Scandinavia.

The brooch, known as the Strickland brooch, was made in the ninth century. It is made from silver and inlaid with gold. It is 11cm in diameter. Careful examination shows that decoration is based on animal designs.

The other two ornaments are from the Sutton Hoo ship burial. The buckle is decorated with interweaving gripping beasts, though the heads of the beasts are not that clear, they can be identified by careful examination.

The shield ornament is a stylised dragon decorated with abstract interweaving designs.

Developments

- The Jorvik helmet is an important example of Anglo-Saxon ornamentation. It was found during the excavations at Coppergate, York, which led to the recreating of the Viking town, Jorvik. However, the helmet is Anglo-Saxon, possibly lost during the battle for York in AD866. Find pictures of the helmet and point out the brass nasal decorated with an interweaving design of 'gripping beasts'. The nasal is gripped in a dragon's head facing down from the top of the helmet.
- Make a copy of the Jorvik helmet. This could be done by building up papier mâché over a balloon and popping the balloon to form the top half of the helmet. The eyeguards and nasal could be cut from card and decorated.
- The helmet has an inscription in Latin. Translated, it reads: *'In the name of our Lord Jesus, the Holy Spirit, God the Father and with all we pray. Amen. Christ.'* Talk about what this tells us.
- Discuss what can be learned about people and life in the past by looking at different kinds of evidence. For example, what can we guess from a helmet that has a religious statement written on it. Did the owner believe that God was on his side? What about the use of Latin? Did all Anglo-Saxons read and write Latin?
- Archaeologists are dependent upon finding historical evidence on which theories can be based and historical interpretations made. Discuss with the children:
  - Where are such objects found? How do the archaeologists decide where to look?
  - Ask the children to think about how useful such finds are as historical evidence.

Anglo-Saxon Ornaments

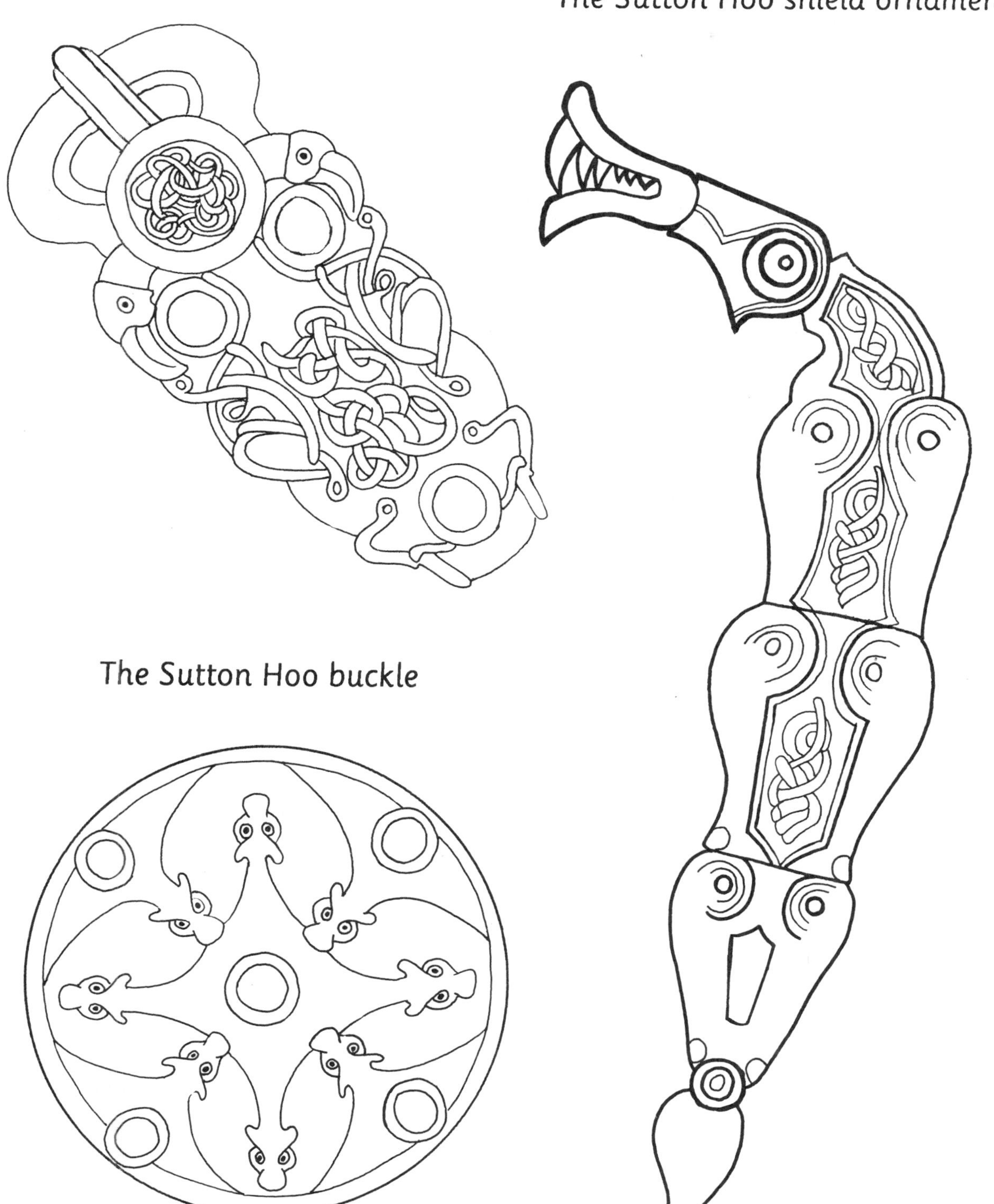

The Sutton Hoo shield ornament

The Sutton Hoo buckle

The Strickland brooch

Manuscript Art - Ideas Page

Aim

To introduce the children to the beauty of Anglo-Saxon manuscript design and calligraphy.

Background

Some of the finest examples of Anglo-Saxon art are the beautifully-illustrated books produced in monasteries, such as Lindisfarne. The majority of these books were burned in Viking raids, or destroyed in the dissolution of the monasteries. However, enough remain to give us an idea of their beauty.

The pages of these books often make use of the interweaving designs that feature in so much Anglo-Saxon art and these are combined with beautifully-coloured pictures and ornate capital letters. They are written in a clear rounded script that is much easier on the eye than the later medieval gothic scripts.

Activity

- The designs on the activity sheet could be used as a resource to enhance presentation of any written work arising from the study of the Anglo-Saxons. For example:
  - The children could begin with draft of a text, perhaps a story version of a farmer's year.
  - To prepare a page for writing, they should rule a 2cm border around a sheet of blank paper.
  - They then could decorate the border using ideas from the resource sheet. A quick way to provide a ready-made border is to photocopy the resource sheet and cut out the centre section.
  - The children should write in their own style, but with a broad-nibbed pen held at 45 degrees. They will need to practise this first. Guidelines could be drawn faintly, or if the paper is transparent enough, laid underneath.
  - The alphabet on the activity sheet can be copied for special purposes, such as titles or the first letters of paragraphs.
  - During a topic on the Anglo-Saxons, each child could produce one or two pages in this way and the pages could be collated and bound to make a class Anglo-Saxon manuscript.

Developments

- Ask the children to look through reference books on Anglo-Saxons and copy down any interesting design motifs. These could then be used in their own designs.
- One of the tools used for writing was the quill pen. Provide a selection of large feathers, cut to a point and slit to resemble a pen nib. Allow the children to experiment: Which ones work best? Can they discover why?
- 'Manuscript' means written by hand.
  - Why were books illustrated in this way?
  - What were they written on?
  - Who would have made them?
  - Who could read them?
  - What was the subject matter of such books?
  - How do we decorate books today?
- Historians used to call the Anglo-Saxon period the 'Dark Ages' because they believed it to be inferior in culture and tradition to the Romans who preceded them and the Normans who came after them. Ask children to consider whether they think this might be true.

Anglo-Saxon culture	Evidence	Dark Ages?	Reason
Song	Caedmon		
Poetry	Beowulf		
Weapons	Sutton Hoo		
Manuscripts	Lindisfarne		

Manuscript Art

Eight ways to help ...

There are hundreds of ideas in this book to enable you to develop and extend the photocopiable pages. Here are just eight ways to help you make the most of the **Ideas Bank** series.

1

Photocopy a page, paste on to card and laminate/cover with sticky-backed plastic to use with groups. The children can now write on the pages using water-based pens which can be washed off.

2

Photocopy on to both sides of the paper, and put another useful activity on the back. Develop a simple filing system so that your colleagues can find relevant sheets and do not duplicate them again.

3

Save the sheets – if the children do not have to cut them up as a part of the activity – and re-use them. Label the sets, and keep them safely in files.

4

Make the most of group work. Children working in small groups need one sheet to discuss between them.

5

Put the sheets inside clear plastic wallets. This means the sheets are easily stored in a binder and will last longer. Again, the children's writing can be wiped away.

6

Use the activity page as an ideas page for yourself. Discuss issues with the class and ask the children to produce artwork and writing.

7

Make an overhead transparency of the page. You and your colleagues can now use the idea time and time again.

8

Ask yourself, "Does every child in this class/group need to deal with/work through this activity page?" If not, don't photocopy it!